Weather Map Handbook

A guide to the Internet, modern forecasting,
and weather technology

Tim Vasquez

First published August 2003
November 2003 layout

First edition

ISBN 0 9706840 4 5

Printed in the United States of America

Weather Graphics Technologies
2110 Slaughter Lane, Suite 115-101, Austin TX 78748
(800) 840-6280 fax (512) 280-6713
Web site: www.weathergraphics.com
support@weathergraphics.com

Contents

ACKNOWLEDGEMENTS

This book, compared to other titles I have written, was a relatively solitary effort, and spanned much of July and early August of 2003. Thanks to Chuck Doswell for assistance on pinning down the source of an older stability index, to Greg Stumpf for clarifying information about NSSL's WSR-88D algorithm developments, and most of all to Shannon Key for helping with several nomograms and proofreading. I also appreciate some insight contributed by Lon Curtis, Stephen Corfidi, John Monteverdi, Paul Markowski, David Blanchard, Patrick Kerrin, and Tim Marshall.

This book attempted to bring in all available meteorological charts, and I would love to hear about omissions so that this can be updated in the next edition. The only omission of a non-regional source that I am aware of is AccuWeather's Professional service. AccuWeather did not reply to my requests to reproduce their charts, and so could not be included.

INTRODUCTION

Weather aficionados, a group which includes just about anyone predisposed to picking up this book, are living in an awesome science-fiction tale. In Chapter One, which began in 1983, the only economical weather data came from NOAA Weather Radio, where a hobbyist would spend ten minutes listening to the voice broadcast to find bits and pieces about what was happening in the towns nearby. For $1000 per month there was the NOAA Weather Wire, which wasn't quite as good as the upscale FAA 604 data feed. Or if you had a costly home computer, you could pay as you go — $1 per minute plus long distance charges would buy downloadable data at 1200 baud from a private vendor. Electronic weather maps could be downloaded as very coarse images in Tektronix 4010 format, viewable only on a good PC with a proprietary terminal software package. For the rest of us without a big wallet, there was CompuServe's Weather forum, which offered the gamut of North American raw observations for about 50 cents per session plus connect charges.

Chapter Two takes place in 2003. The technological magic of the Internet and cheap technology have brought the global weather telecommunications infrastructure to every person's desktop. It's possible to obtain almost every shred of global weather data at lightning-fast speeds. Vast graphics storehouses from models and weather display programs are available at the click of a mouse. What do you do with these incredible resources?

It is my hope that this book provides an excellent introduction for the enthusiastic novice as well as a valuable reference book for seasoned hobbyists. At the very least it is designed to help guide readers through the vast sea of weather data which is getting deeper every day. The pitfalls, the strengths, and the quirks of each product are pointed out, and informal conventions such as coloring and symbology are defined.

It's an exciting time to enjoy the field of meteorology! Technology simply has not caught up with the complexity of atmospheric physics. Every five years, most weather agencies pour millions of dollars into major computer upgrades. The bureaucrats tout them as a panacea, but in reality all they do is give us bigger and better tools. Regardless of the quality of tools that are produced, the challenging job of forecasting must still be done. This leaves plenty of room for the person who wants to learn the art and mystery of forecasting using 21st-century technology, applying experience, intuition, and pattern recognition from past weather events. A background in differential equations and a college degree are not necessary to make an accurate forecast. All it takes is the desire to participate and the enthusiasm to tackle an advanced subject when things are unclear. Little by little one can become a master at this sophisticated, captivating area of science. It's the ultimate puzzle!

TIM VASQUEZ
August 2003
Austin, Texas

A second edition will almost certainly be printed. Corrections and suggestions are gladly welcomed. Send them along to <tim@weathergraphics.com>.

Basic Forecasting Concepts

The world is at your fingertips. The high-speed cablemodem is toasty, the lights flickering confidently. Thousands of charts are at your disposal, much more data than a typical National Weather Service office could dream about in 1990. Yet you can't help but to sit there and ask: *What do I look at?*

What's your objective?

Certainly you could browse randomly through dozens of Internet weather charts. In fact every time you sat down you could pull up each and every chart listed in this book! However, this is inefficient and does little to provide you with meaningful information. There is no way the human brain can sift coherently through hundreds of charts.

The question you must ask yourself is *what am I trying to accomplish?* The answer, combined with a rough understanding of meteorology, will help you seek out the ingredients and patterns you are looking for, and in turn this book will help you figure out what charts you should concentrate on.

For example, if you are sailing, are you trying to find the best wind patterns? If so, you'll be focusing on surface charts, and will also examine upper-level charts for features that could locally strengthen the surface

pressure gradient. Are you a chaser expecting storms to fire any minute? The ingredients that would favor initiation in a specific location would include convergence and the presence of cumulus towers. Thus you will be looking at small-scale surface plots and visible satellite imagery.

Picking a good web site

Your next challenge will be deciding what web sites work best for you. It's always best to research your options on a fair-weather day. There's nothing worse than scrambling to find the best radar chart when a historic storm is about to punch through the state!

☐ **How timely are the updates?** Your favorite site might have the best graphics, but if 06Z rolls around and the RUC isn't yet posted, it's a good idea to have a backup in mind.

☐ **Are you getting the fields and detail you want?** Do you want wind barbs with that RUC surface prog? If so UCAR or NCEP might be best, otherwise College of DuPage or Unisys might be your choice. Are you happy with stick-figure geography or do you like cool, antialiased borders with terrain? Do you like the power of multiple fields, or is simplicity your cup of tea? Look around!

☐ **Do the charts print well?** If you love making printouts and posting them on your bulletin board, charts with black backgrounds will look atrocious and will drain your ink-cartridge budget. See if the website offers a "printer friendly" option for each map. This provides the same graphic with a white background.

☐ **Will software products do a better job?** Depending on what kind of chart analysis you are doing, Digital Atmosphere (the author's plotting software), RAOB, Sharp, and other standalone programs may be much more suited to the task at hand and give more professional results. Dabble a bit with each of them.

☐ **Are there newer sources?** Weather charts on the web change monthly. Listen in on mailing lists such as WX-TALK and examine other people's bookmarks to see what they are using. Check in on sites you don't typically use. Even some of the Web sites in this book may be obsolete after several months. If you get a "file not found" error you can often find the new charts by deleting the right site of the URL up to the last solidus, trying again. Keep shortening the URL in this manner until you get to a working page.

☐ **Bookmark your favorite sites.** There's nothing more aggravating than trying to remember that obscure website that gave you an excellent weather chart. Maintain a special bookmark folder and add to it as you find new charts you like.

Weather basics: back to school

Although a complete discussion about forecasting is far beyond the scope of this book, a brief overview of forecasting process is warranted. The overwhelming question that most forecasters try to solve daily is, "Where will there be clouds and precipitation?"

Obviously the clouds and precipitation may not have formed yet, so looking for the underlying causes, rather than what's there already, is the crux of the forecast process. In either case, the clouds and precipitation are caused by some type of lift, often called *ascent* by meteorologists. Stratiform rain is caused by slow, large-scale ascent of a very humid air mass. Convective showers and rain can be aided by this process, but depend much more on the presence of instability (very warm air underlying cold air). The ascent occurs in the form of very small pockets of rising motion, the size of a cumuliform cloud.

Sources of ascent

Slow, large-scale (synoptic-scale) ascent is one of the easiest problems for amateur forecasters, professionals, and numerical weather models to tackle. It occurs over such a large area that the air mass characteristics are sampled quite well by surface and radiosonde stations. In most cases, large-scale ascent is revealed in many different ways, including:

☐ **Upper-level forcing**, often called "dynamics". This occurs when air is no longer in geostrophic balance, typically because of thermal contrasts in the air mass below. The air is forced to seek out sinking or rising motion to try to compensate for the lack of geostrophic balance. When the response is divergence in the upper atmosphere, which removes mass from the column and lowers surface pressures, air tends to rise to "fill the void". The famous "four-cell concept" of vertical motion and Q-vector divergence are all indicators of upper-level forcing.

☐ **Isentropic lift**, which is most prominent when air parcels are travelling over rapidly varying air mass temperatures. The parcels must rise or sink in order to conserve their potential temperature.

☐ **Surface convergence**, due to a clash in low-level wind direction or a low pressure area, causes ascent. Air converges and is forced to rise. This is closely related to orographic lift.

☐ **Orographic lift**, where air is forced higher and higher as it travels along ascending terrain. This can occur on scales anywhere from ascent up a mountain to long runs of ascent measuring

1000 miles or more on the Great Plains. The longer runs of ascent are often referred to as upslope flow.

Air may also rise in a convectively unstable air mass to form showers and thunderstorms. This occurs when very cold air overlies warm, moist air in the low levels. Intense sunshine is not necessarily a requirement for convective instability. It can come from differential advection, for example when cold air overruns an area aloft, or from heating of an air mass by a warm body of water, such as Great Lakes lake-effect snowstorms.

Finding areas of ascent

Each of these mechanisms has indicators, patterns, and characteristics which show up on standard weather charts. For example, warm air advection (WAA) occurs where winds and pressure gradient are bringing in warmer air. This tends to imply the presence of isentropic lift. At the 500 mb level, cyclonic vorticity advection (CVA), also known as positive vorticity advection (PVA) in the Northern Hemisphere, is often associated with upper-level divergence, which implies upward motion.

Although there are model charts that depict omega, which is the value of vertical velocity, these do not provide an easy, cookie-cutter solution. The omega fields tend to be noisy and difficult to scrutinize. Furthermore, they say nothing about why the lift or subsidence is occurring, its character, and what implications it has for the forecast area. A wise weather forecaster will look past these nondescript "headlines" and open up the charts to get a full understanding of what is happening.

Unfortunately this is where the discussion must end. To jump into these issues in much greater detail, see titles like the author's *Weather Forecasting Handbook*, Jack William's *The Weather Book*, and Stanley David Gedzelman's 1980 *Science and Wonders of the Atmosphere* (if you can still get it!).

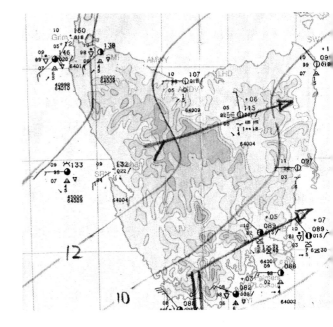

Above: Analysis chart for Tasmania. *(Australian Bureau of Meteorology)*

Previous page: Forecasters working on a severe thunderstorm problem at the Fort Worth WSFO in Texas.

Other valuable resources

Though book knowledge will take you far, there are a few other things you need to know before you get started. Practice often, and get familiar with the UTC time zone!

☐ **Pencils and crayons.** If you are planning to dig deep into chart analysis, a good supply of HB and 2H pencils, as well as crayons, are a great idea. Keep a box full of them near your analysis table. A good-quality drafting eraser will help scrub out mistakes. Various colored highlighters have all kinds of uses, including the ability to make working marks in your atlases without creating too much of a mess. Finally, a divider is handy for translating map distances on map scales. Most of these items can be purchased at art and hobby shops, office supply stores, and architectural supply companies.

☐ **Atlases.** Topography and geography plays into all aspects of meteorology, from orographic lift to storm reports from small towns. National Weather Service analysis desks are characterized by their excellent assortment of beat-up atlases. Likewise, keep a few titles near your desk. For the United States, the *Mobil Road Atlas and Travel Planner* edges out ahead of the standard Rand McNally and AAA atlases since it offers full map coverage at a constant scale. This makes it very easy to track weather systems and visualize their size as they progress across state and national borders. For worldwide topographic views the *Planet Earth Macmillan World Atlas* maps out the world at two sets of equivalent scales. Try not to be edgy about drawing in your atlases and bending the spine to get a better look; after all they're there to be used rather than to collect dust in your bookshelf, and used replacements are cheap.

☐ **Coordinated Universal Time (UTC).** The UTC time zone is used religiously in weather forecasting, and you will not get far without knowing how to convert your time zone to UTC and back. UTC time is simply the time in London, England, not counting for their daylight saving time. See Table 1 for exact conversions.

☐ **Practice, practice, practice!** Skills only come with experience, and experience cannot be built if you are taking a casual, uninvolved approach to the weather. Supplement your experience by building a good weather library and using it.

Below: What would a typical National Weather Service office look like if the clock was turned back over 100 years? Here in January 1899 we see a local U.S. Weather Bureau office in Buffalo, New York. This fledgling organization had been transferred from the Army Signal Corps only eight years earlier. Only weeks later the U.S. would endure its coldest arctic outbreak in recorded history, a record that still stands today. *(NOAA)*

Table 1. Time zone conversions. The "code" is the military designator, typically expressed as the phonetic word for each letter (Alpha, Bravo, etc). For further information see <www.timeanddate.com> and <www.mindspring.com/~gwil/tconcept.html>

When standard time is in effect (no local daylight saving or summer time)

Code	If your time zone is	To convert from UTC to local	Examples
Y	International Date Line West (IDLW)	subtract 12 hours	(none)
X	Samoa Standard Time (SST)	subtract 11 hours	Apia, Niue, Midway, Pago Pago
W	Hawaii Standard Time (HST)	subtract 10 hours	Honolulu, Hilo, Tahiti
V	Alaska Standard Time (AKST)	subtract 9 hours	Anchorage, Fairbanks, Barrow
U	Pacific Standard Time (PST)	subtract 8 hours	Los Angeles, Seattle, Vancouver
T	Mountain Standard Time (MST)	subtract 7 hours	Phoenix, Salt Lake City, Denver, Calgary
S	Central Standard Time (CST)	subtract 6 hours	Dallas, Chicago, Minneapolis, Winnipeg
R	Eastern Standard Time (EST)	subtract 5 hour	New York City, Boston, Toronto
Q	Atlantic Standard (AST), Western Brazil (WST)	subtract 4 hours	Halifax, Moncton, Bermuda, Thule
-	Newfoundland Standard Time (NST)	subtract 3.5 hours	Stephenville, St. Johns
P	Brazil Time (BRT), Western Greenland Time (WGT)	subtract 3 hours	Nuuk, Buenos Aires, Rio de Janeiro
O	Fernando de Noronha Time (FNT)	subtract 2 hours	Noronha
N	Azores Time (AZOT), Eastern Greenland (EGT)	subtract 1 hour	Scoresbysund, Cape Verde
Z	Greenwich Mean Time (GMT)	no change	London, Glasgow, Dublin, Lisbon, Dakar
A	Central European Time (CET), W. Africa Time (WAT)	add 1 hour	Paris, Frankfurt, Stockholm
B	E. European Time (EET), Central Africa Time (CAT)	add 2 hours	Helsinki, Kiev, Sofia, Athens
C	Arabian Standard Time (AST), E. Africa Time (EAT)	add 3 hours	Moscow, Baghdad, Aden, Nairobi
D	Gulf Standard Time (GST), Russia Zone 4 (ZP4)	add 4 hours	Samara, Dubai, Muscat
E	Pakistan Time (PKT), Russia Zone 5 (ZP5)	add 5 hours	Yekaterinburg
-	India Standard Time (IST)	add 5.5 hours	Calcutta, New Delhi, Bombay
F	Bangladesh Time (BDT), Russia Zone 6 (ZP6)	add 6 hours	Omsk, Dhaka
G	Indochina Time (ICT)	add 7 hours	Krasnoyarsk, Bangkok, Jakarta, Hanoi
H	Aust. Western Std. Time (AWST), China Std. (CST)	add 8 hours	Perth (WA), Manila, Taipei, Beijing
I	Japan Standard Time (JST), Korea Standard (KST)	add 9 hours	Tokyo, Seoul, Yakutsk
-	Australia Central Standard Time (ACST)	add 9.5 hours	Darwin, SA/NT
K	Australia Eastern Standard Time (AEST)	add 10 hours	Sydney, QL/ACT/NSW/VIC/TAS
L	Magadan Time (MAGT), New Caledonia (NCT)	add 11 hours	Magadan, Noumea, Ponape
M	New Zealand Standard Time (NZST)	add 12 hours	Kamchatka, Auckland, Kwajalein, Fiji
-	Tonga Time (TOT), Phoenix Isl. Time (PHOT)	add 13 hours	Enderbury, Tongatapu
-	Line Island Time (LINT)	add 14 hours	Kiritimati

When local daylight saving or summer time is in effect

Code	If your time zone is	To convert from UTC to local	Examples
U	Alaska Daylight Time (AKDT)	subtract 8 hours	Anchorage, Fairbanks, Barrow
T	Pacific Daylight Time (PDT)	subtract 7 hours	Los Angeles, San Francisco, Vancouver
S	Mountain Daylight Time (MDT)	subtract 6 hours	Denver, Salt Lake City, Calgary
R	Central Daylight Time (CDT)	subtract 5 hours	Dallas, Chicago, Minneapolis, Winnipeg
Q	Eastern Daylight Time (EDT)	subtract 4 hours	New York City, Boston, Toronto
P	Atlantic Daylight Time (ADT)	subtract 3 hours	Halifax, Moncton, Bermuda
A	British/Irish Summer Time (BST)	add 1 hour	London, Belfast, Glasgow
B	Central European Summer Time (CEST)	add 2 hours	Frankfurt, Paris, Oslo, Zurich, Warsaw
C	Eastern European Summer Time (EEST)	add 3 hours	Helsinki, Athens, Sofia, Kiev
D	Moscow Summer Time (MSD)	add 4 hours	Moscow
K	Japan Daylight Time (JDT)	add 10 hours	Tokyo
-	Australian Central Daylight Time (ACDT)	add 10.5 hours	Adelaide, SA
L	Australian Eastern Daylight Time (AEDT)	add 11 hours	Sydney, ACT/NSW/VIC/TAS

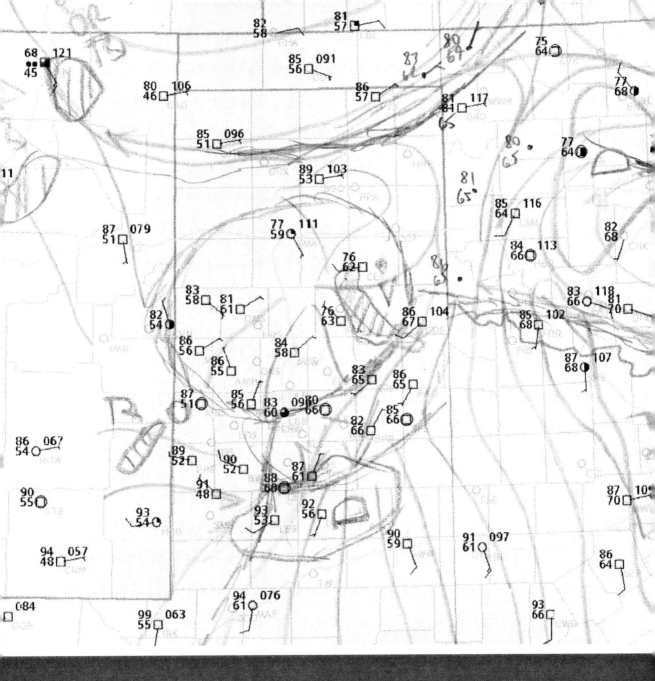

OBSERVATIONAL CHARTS

Above: An actual surface analysis used in a short-range storm forecast demonstrates that the chart is a canvas for thought.

Observational Charts

A weather product is often used only for its intrinsic value. What is the temperature? Is it raining over Pittsburgh? Is there a threat of clouds for tonight's star party? Will the flight crew have good headwinds?

In a more organized forecast setting, weather charts and products become tools rather than indicators. Therefore this book attempts to explain not only how to interpret them but also to find the subtle signals, patterns, and trends that may have a much greater impact on the forecast. This is the science and art of meteorological diagnosis. Developing the talent for diagnosis requires a little philosophical insight and the willing participation of the forecaster.

The chart analysis process

Some excellent papers have been written on the philosophy behind using weather charts. Two of them are, "The Role of Diagnosis in Weather Forecasting" (1986) by Charles Doswell III and Robert Maddox; and "The Human Element in Weather Forecasting" (1986) by Charles Doswell III, both online at <www.cimms.ou.edu/~doswell>. In these essays, Doswell and Maddox identified two separate steps that must occur before a prognosis (forecast) can be made: analysis and diagnosis.

The first step, *analysis*, is the identification of ingredients in the atmosphere. It is the process of drawing lines and identifying fronts, lows, highs, wind shift lines, jets, and air masses. A computer may assume a lot of the analysis procedures. Following this, a process called *diagnosis* is performed. This is composed of thought, ideas, and conclusions. It is the process of visualizing the completed analysis and relating it to other products. Diagnosis is also the precursor to a coherent, robust forecast.

Unfortunately in today's computer-driven age, some forecasters complete the analysis but fail to complete a diagnosis. Quick glances at the maps and reliance on computer-drawn isopleths do not constitute diagnosis. As a result, the misguided forecast process inevitably leans toward very heavy emphasis on numerical models. The balance in the forecast process is spelled out surprisingly clear in forecast discussions, case studies, and even technical papers.

There are countless situations where important ingredients are resolved not through the models but only through careful analysis and diagnosis. One case in point is a jet max moving out of New Mexico on 3 May 1999, linked to a deadly tornado outbreak near Oklahoma City, and initially detected only by the Tucumcari NM wind profiler. Fortunately this clue was detected in plenty of time.

A debate has sometimes emerged among some of the best operational forecasters: is it absolutely necessary to put pencil to paper and "hand-analyze" the chart? The consensus is a resounding "yes", with a few rare exceptions. There is nothing to be lost by forcing yourself to scrutinize the data in better detail. It's pure common sense!

Even so, hand analysis only works when the forecaster makes an effort to think about the data. Drawing lines with a closed or distracted mind accomplishes nothing more than drawing lines. Make an effort to visualize the meaning of the data as you put pencil to paper. Glance at the station plots as you go, picturing the weather and contrasting it to conditions you see nearby. The chart is not a picture to be drawn; it is a canvas for thought.

Frontal placement

Fronts are one of the most basic components of a weather chart, as they highlight *baroclinic zones*, where temperature advection is taking place and atmospheric energy is at work. A front is always drawn with its barbs or pips facing the direction of movement. Table 2 details the styles used for depicting a front.

Fronts are always placed on the *warm side of a temperature gradient.* This makes perfect logical sense, as when we picture a cold air mass moving into a region, the front occurs when the temperature first begins falling, not when the temperature drop is complete. When warm air is invading, it is not quite as intuitive, but the most basic weather books demonstrate that the warm front passes after the temperature has finished climbing (not counting the effects of diurnal heating, of course).

Drylines are sharp boundaries between a moist tropical air mass and a very dry continental airmass, usually originating from higher terrain. They are common in the southern Great Plains of the United States but may also be found in India, the Sahel, and Australia. The dryline is always located on the *moist side of the dewpoint gradient.* The barbs point toward the direction of the dryline's movement.

Finally, troughs and other features can be sketched in. However it should be noted that it is important to spend more time refining your position of the feature than attempting to categorize it. The feature can be revisited later in the diagnosis process and may be much more meaningful then.

The symbols for fronts and boundaries are shown in Table 2. Throughout this book, various styles and colors for other parameters are recommended. Most of these assume you are marking on white charts. For black (on-screen) graphics, these colors are all still valid, except that white and black are reversed.

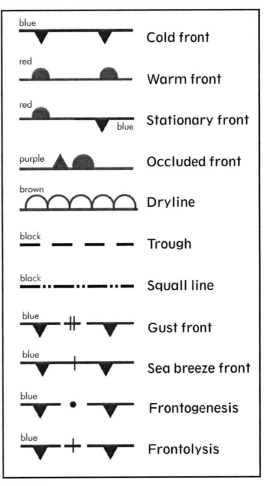

Table 2. Conventions for drawing fronts and boundaries. The scheme for a gust front and sea breeze front is adopted from Young and Fritsch (1989).

Quick tip

Want professional-looking charts? You can print giant 22″ x 17″ charts without breaking the bank. The Epson 1520 inkjet printer ($499) has been around for about six years, and handles these massive sheets of paper with no problem. The trouble is finding the paper! You won't find it at Office Max, Office Depot, or most paper shops. The secret is to get it from an architectural and drafting supply company. You'll likely have to get it cut to size. The cost should be no more than 15 cents per sheet.

Surface Chart

The surface chart is the backbone of weather forecasting and is the most familiar map to anyone who has dabbled in meteorology. The first regular map was a surface chart drawn in 1815 by German scientist Heinrich W. Brandes.

Nowadays, surface weather readings are collected largely by automated sensors in the United States. The report is encoded in METAR or SYNOP format, a specification laid down by the World Meteorological Organization, and is transmitted to regional data centers. From there the information makes its way to end users. Users who have access to this data can hand-plot or display a variety of surface charts.

The biggest advantage of the surface chart is that data is available quite frequently: as often as six hours in remote regions and as much as every 20 minutes in North America. A less obvious but extremely important use of the chart is to search for imbalances that reflect processes occurring aloft, which may not be reflected by the coarse radiosonde data that is only available every twelve hours. For example, pressure fall centers or very gusty winds may be closely linked to areas of strong upper-level forcing moving with the upper-level flow.

Although winds closely follow the pressure (height) lines on upper-level charts, this is not necessarily the case on the surface chart. The winds may turn an average of 30 degrees toward low pressure. This is because the effect of friction is much more pronounced, which diminishes the Coriolis effect and allows air to move more directly toward low pressure. The effect is not so strong on ocean surfaces due to weaker friction.

A recommended sequence for analyzing the surface chart is to look for obvious fronts and boundaries and sketch them in lightly. Then sketch in isobars lightly with the pencil. Use the isobars and other indicators to further refine front and boundary positions. Then "harden in" the final position of the front. Following this, "harden in" the isobars, forcing them to kink along the front. While this process is underway, never forget to spend time visualizing what is seen on the chart, feeling the data as you go. This will help make your diagnosis complete.

Great sites with real-time data for this product . . .
- HPC — **www.hpc.ncep.noaa.gov/html/sfc2body.html**
- UCAR — **www.rap.ucar.edu/weather/surface**
- College of DuPage — **weather.cod.edu/analysis**
- Hong Kong — **www.hko.gov.hk/wxinfo/currwx/wxcht.htm**
- NOAA/SPC — **www.spc.noaa.gov/exper/mesoanalysis**
- Unisys — **weather.unisys.com/surface**

■ Surface plots are explained in Table 1A in the Appendix.

■ Observations of surface weather are collected by automated sensors (such as ASOS in the United States) as well as human and human-augmented measurements. The data is transmitted in METAR and SYNOP format to regional data centers and to end users. From there, charts can be displayed in a geographic format.

■ In the United States, temperature and dewpoint values are almost always in degrees Fahrenheit. Outside the United States they are in degrees Celsius.

■ Data is almost always available every six hours, as is common with the SYNOP format used worldwide or every 20 to 60 minutes with the METAR format.

■ **Fields**
- Isobars are drawn in solid black every 4 mb or 0.05 in Hg.
- Isotherms (optional) are drawn every 2 C° or 5 F°.
- Other fields may be added as needed.

■ **Features**
- High and low pressure centers are marked using, respectively, a large blue "H" or a large red "L". The center pressure value may be labelled below the H or L, typically in tens and units of a millibar.
- Fronts are drawn in blue and red using standard notation.
- Trough axes are drawn as a thick black dashed line.
- Drylines are drawn as a thick brown line with hollow pips connected to one another, facing toward the moisture.

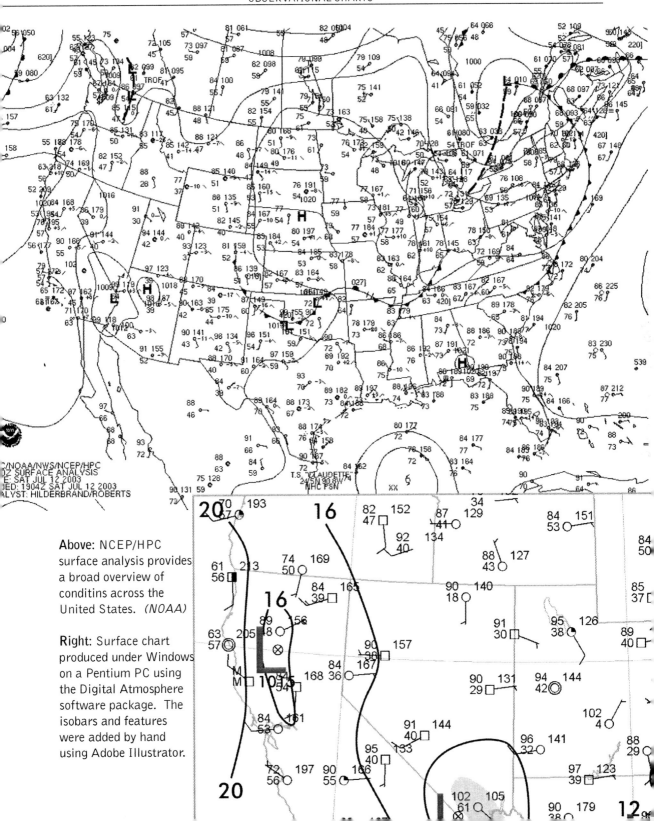

/NOAA/NWS/NCEP/HPC
Z SURFACE ANALYSIS
E: SAT JUL 12 2003
ED: 1904Z SAT JUL 12 2003
ALYST: HILDERBRAND/ROBERTS

Above: NCEP/HPC surface analysis provides a broad overview of conditins across the United States. *(NOAA)*

Right: Surface chart produced under Windows on a Pentium PC using the Digital Atmosphere software package. The isobars and features were added by hand using Adobe Illustrator.

850 mb Chart

The 850 mb level is located at about 5000 ft MSL, assuming a standard atmosphere, however it can vary by several hundred feet or more. The key phrase is *MSL*: mean sea level. This means that along flat land near sea level, the 850 mb level will be about 5000 ft above the ground. At Salt Lake City, 4300 ft elevation, the 850 mb level is only about 700 feet above the ground! And in the Rocky Mountains, the 850 mb level is far underground. It can be said that the 850 mb level may be found in one of three places: underground, within the planetary boundary layer, or in the free atmosphere.

The planetary boundary layer (PBL) is that part of the troposphere in contact with the ground. A typical depth is about 2000 ft. The PBL is strongly influenced by the earth's surface through heating, drag, and evapotranspiration. In reality, the top of the PBL can range from the Earth's surface on a clear, cold night to 10,000 ft AGL or more given a windy, unstable, uncapped air mass with very strong heating.

Therefore depending on the surface elevation, the time of day, the season, and the ongoing weather regime, the 850 mb level, if not underground, will be within the PBL or within the free atmosphere. It is useful to a sense of which layer the radiosonde is representing and get familiar with all of the radiosonde station elevations in your region to see how high the 850 mb level usually is at each site. It is also important to bear in mind that the PBL and free atmosphere can seem to merge, especially during the summer in weak wind patterns, and drawing a distinction may not be important.

When it comes time to put the pencil to the maps, the most popular use for the 850 mb chart is to locate frontal systems, particularly when their positions are not clear on the surface chart. Remember that frontal surfaces slope up and into cold air, therefore the 850 mb front will almost always be found poleward of the surface front. There are some exceptions, particularly on the Plains, where cold fronts will move much faster aloft than near the ground, and this may result in a cold front being placed equatorward of the surface front.

During the spring months, the 850 mb chart helps paint out the configuration of the low-level jet (LLJ). This feature is common before severe weather outbreaks and typically stretches from the Gulf of Mexico coastline into the central United States.

Great sites with real-time data for this product . . .
○ NWS DIFAX — **weather.noaa.gov/fax/nwsfax.html**
○ UCAR — **www.rap.ucar.edu/weather/upper**
○ College of DuPage — **weather.cod.edu/analysis**
○ NOAA/SPC — **www.spc.noaa.gov/exper/mesoanalysis**
○ Unisys — **weather.unisys.com/upper_air**

■ 850 mb is usually at 5000 ft MSL

■ Upper air plots are explained in Table 1B in the Appendix.

■ At 850 mb, areas of warm advection are associated with ascent, while cold advection is associated with descent.

■ In many areas of the western United States and in higher terrain, the 850 mb level is below ground. Plots will contain missing winds and temperatures, but an extrapolated height reading and height change value will be available.

■ **Fields**
- Height contours are drawn as solid black lines every 30 m (3 dam) using 150 dam as a base value (147, 150, 153, etc). Labels are in dam.
- Isotherms are drawn as dashed red lines every 5 C°, however 2 C° and 4 C° intervals are common.
- The type of moisture analysis (optional) is contingent on the type of weather regime:
  -- In stratiform situations, a relative humidity parameter is recommended. Shade all areas in green with dewpoint depressions below 5 C° (this is roughly a 75% relative humidity).
  -- In convective situations, use an absolute humidity parameter. Figure the dewpoint for each station and draw isodrosotherms.

■ **Features**
- Low level jet axes (narrow bands of strong winds exceeding 40 kt) should be drawn as a thick red arrow.
- Moisture axes may be drawn as thick, wavy green lines. Pencil is best.
- Fronts should be drawn in standard blue and red colors. Since this is an upper-air chart, do not shade the barbs and pips.

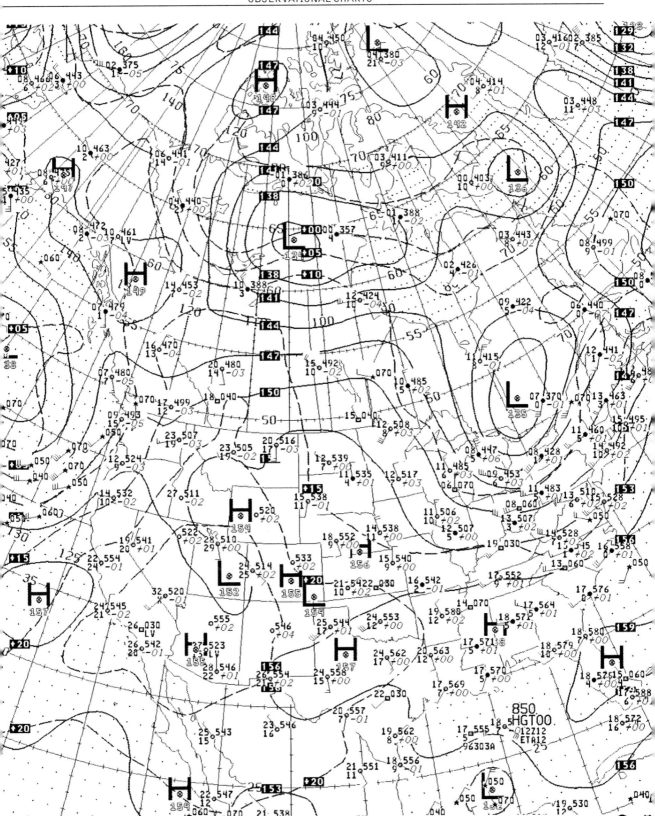

700 mb Chart

The 700 mb level is roughly at 10,000 ft MSL. This is considered to be somewhere between the lower and middle troposphere. At higher radiosonde stations such as Denver and Salt Lake City, the 700 mb level is only about 5000 ft above the ground and may be within part of the planetary boundary layer during the warm season (see section on the 850 mb level). This is especially true of the higher mountainous regions.

Weather systems at 700 mb typically take on an open, broad look compared to the patterns at lower levels. The fronts are usually found further poleward compared to the 850 mb and surface charts, owing to the slope of fronts up and into the cold air. This relationship can help place the low-level front when the 700 mb chart shows a thermal gradient and the 850 mb and surface charts don't have a clear position.

Considering that the vast majority of cloud cover in a developing frontal weather system occurs in the 5,000 to 15,000 ft MSL range, humidity is a favorite quantity for measuring the extent of synoptic-scale lift and moisture. Relative humidity values of 70% or dewpoint depressions of 5 C° or less at 700 mb are considered synonymous with overcast cloud cover. The relative humidity value is usually expressed on model output panels, while the dewpoint depression is shown on upper-air plots. When areas exceeding these threshold values are shaded in green, a definition of the area and shape of strongest upper-level forcing emerges. A "wrapped" structure may even be seen on the charts, matching quite well with the cloud bands observed on satellite imagery.

In springtime thunderstorm situations, the 700 mb level is usually within the heart of the elevated mixed layer (EML), a broad area of warm, dry air originating from the southwestern United States that is lofted eastward into the central United States. The air at this level is often warmer than that below it, which provides an inversion, or "cap", that either prevents thunderstorms altogether or suppresses them until afternoon when heating and instability are maximized. Therefore the 700 mb isotherm pattern can help define the coverage and strength of the EML. The axis of highest 700 mb temperatures can help define the axis of the cap, if one can make the assumption that convective parcel temperatures and low-level convergence are relatively similar throughout the entire region.

Great sites with real-time data for this product . . .
- NWS DIFAX — **weather.noaa.gov/fax/nwsfax.html**
- UCAR — **www.rap.ucar.edu/weather/upper**
- College of DuPage — **weather.cod.edu/analysis**
- NOAA/SPC — **www.spc.noaa.gov/exper/mesoanalysis**
- Unisys — **weather.unisys.com/upper_air**

■ 700 mb is usually at about 10,000 ft MSL.

■ Upper air plots are explained in Table 1B in the Appendix.

■ Surface lows tend to move at about 70% of the 700 mb wind speed above the low.

■ Winds at 700 mb that are perpendicular to a surface front suggest a katafront, which tends to produce weather ahead of the front. Winds at 700 mb parallel to a surface front suggest an anafront, with weather behind the front.

■ **Fields**
- Height contours are drawn as solid black lines every 30 meters (3 dam) using 300 dam as a base value (297, 300, 303, etc). Labels are in dam.
- Isotherms are dashed red lines every 5 C°. Intervals of 2 C° or 4 C° are common.

■ **Features**
- Areas of significant moisture (dewpoint depression of 5 C° or less) may be shaded in green.
- Jets axes are represented by a thick red arrow.
- Fronts should be drawn in standard blue and red colors. Since this is an upper-air chart, do not shade the barbs and pips.
- Short wave trough axes are drawn as thick black straight lines.
- Short wave ridge axes are drawn as thick black zig-zag lines.
- Col. Robert Miller's Severe Weather Analysis Notes suggests coloring jets and moisture in brown for this level to signify that they apply to 700 mb.

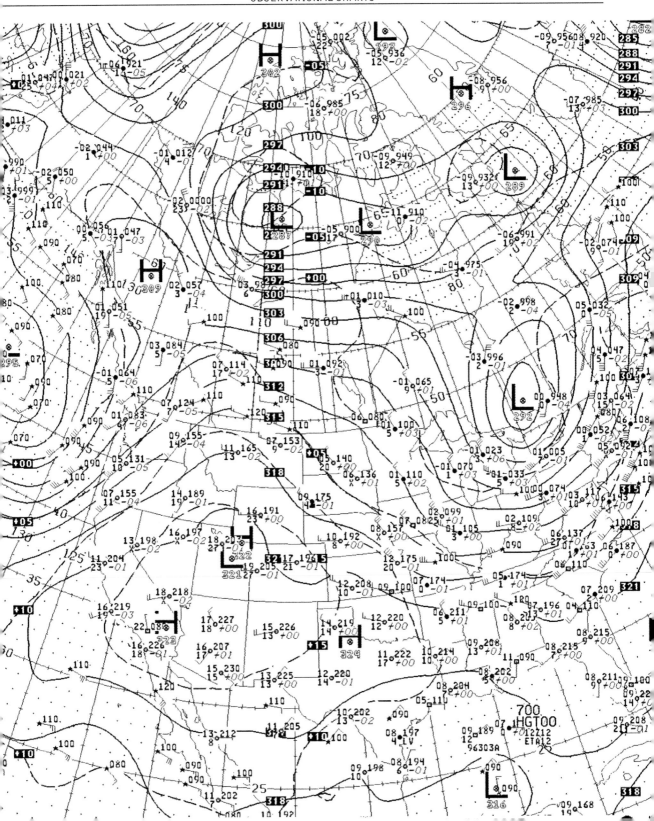

500 mb Chart

Except perhaps in polar regions, the 500 mb level is considered the middle of the troposphere. It exists at a height of about 18,000 ft MSL, and so is nearly always within the free atmosphere and not part of a planetary boundary layer. At this level, forecasters see an excellent mix of small-scale and large-scale systems. At the large scale, the upper-level jet pattern begins emerging, painting out the regions of strongest baroclinicity (energy available to the atmosphere). Superimposed on this are a series of large troughs and ridges. The troughs correspond to very cold air masses, while the ridges exist above areas of warmth.

At even smaller scales we find the notorious *short waves*. These are small-scale troughs and ridges embedded in the large-scale flow which are just barely resolved in the existing radiosonde network. Short waves are reflections of important thermal perturbations in the air mass beneath, whose influence easily translates to higher levels. These perturbations, if a strong thermal gradient is present in the lower troposphere, often go on to amplify the short wave which in turn deepens the short wave, which in turn imparts more energy to the system beneath. This is a chain reaction called "self development" and is broken only when the system finally occludes and washes out the thermal gradient. The short wave trough, by this time, has often deepened into an upper-level low.

Short waves are located using either a vorticity field or looking for wind shifts. On standard upper-air analyses, vorticity overlays are often not available. The vorticity fields are largely a product of numerical weather prediction output, and the short waves tend to lie along elongations of vorticity axes, particularly those that cross the flow in a perpendicular orientation. The short wave will tend to be located along a boundary oriented in a perpendicular fashion across the 500 mb flow which separates two stations with a sharp wind shift. A cyclonic wind shift defines a short wave trough, while an anticyclonic wind shift indicates the presence of a short wave ridge.

Finally, it is crucial to make that distinction between a "short wave" and a "short wave trough", because the term short wave applies to both. Also short waves can sometimes be resolved at lower levels, such at the 700 mb level, and they stack downward toward the warmer air.

- 500 mb is usually at a height of about 18,000 ft MSL.

- Upper air plots are explained in Table 1B in the Appendix.

- Surface lows tend to move at about 50% of the 500 mb wind speed above the low.

■ Fields
- Height contours are drawn as solid black lines every 60 m (6 dam) using 570 dam as a base value (564, 570, 576, etc). Labels are in dam.
- Absolute vorticity contours are machine-produced and are typically drawn as dashed black lines every $2*10^{-5}$ sec.
- Isotherms (optional) are dashed red lines every 5 C°. Intervals of 2 C° or 4 C° are common.

■ Features
- High and low height centers are plotted as a large black "H" or "L", with the decameter value below it.
- Areas of PVA are shaded red.
- Areas of NVA are shaded blue.
- Short wave trough axes are drawn as thick black straight lines.
- Short wave ridge axes are drawn as thick black zig-zag lines.
- Jet axes are drawn as a thick red line.
- Col. Robert Miller's Severe Weather Analysis Notes suggests a blue color for any jet depiction to signify that the markings are for 500 mb.

Great sites with real-time data for this product . . .
- ❍ NWS DIFAX — **weather.noaa.gov/fax/nwsfax.html**
- ❍ UCAR — **www.rap.ucar.edu/weather/upper**
- ❍ College of DuPage — **weather.cod.edu/analysis**
- ❍ NOAA/SPC — **www.spc.noaa.gov/exper/mesoanalysis**
- ❍ Unisys — **weather.unisys.com/upper_air**

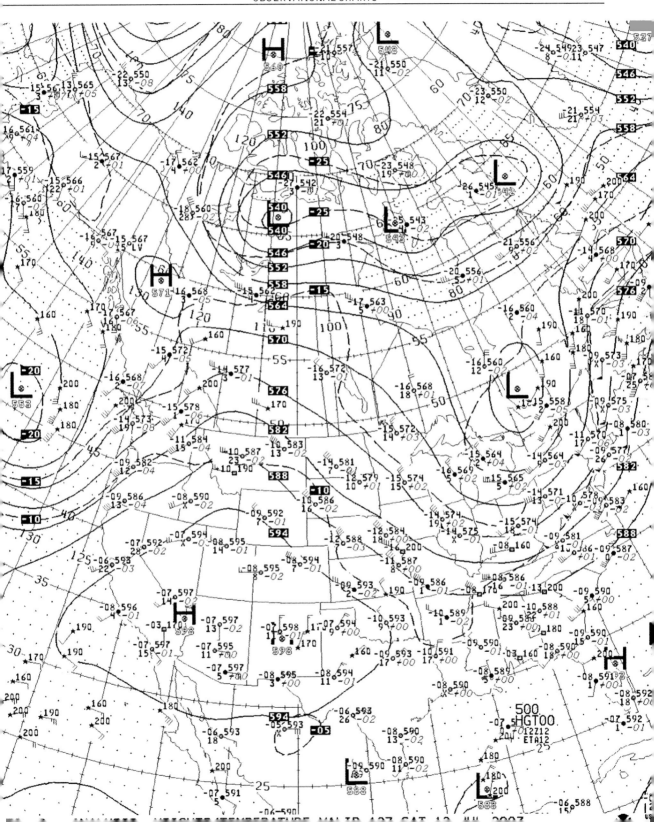

300/250/200 mb Chart

The practicing meteorologist always wants to have a glance at the upper tropospheric conditions, as the polar front jet lies in its topmost portions. Unfortunately picking a level is complicated, because the top of the troposphere (the tropopause) in temperate latitudes ranges in height from 30,000 ft during the winter to 45,000 ft during the summer.

Therefore, given the standard levels of 300 mb (30,000 ft MSL), 250 mb (34,000 ft MSL), and 200 mb (39,000 ft MSL), it is necessary to choose different charts depending on the season to find most representative "upper tropospheric chart". During the winter, 300 mb is used. In the transition seasons of autumn and spring, the 250 mb chart is preferred. In the summer, the 200 mb is selected. The others are discarded as they are either too low or tap into the stratosphere where the polar jet is rapidly weakened with height. Though there is little use for stratospheric charts, some studies have been published on stratospheric warm sinks and cold domes, which have ties to areas of upper divergence and convergence, respectively.

Overall, the axis of strongest winds paints out the jet stream. This pattern is by far the highlight of the upper tropospheric chart, and defines the weather regime that is in place. Long waves are formed by the very broad troughs and ridges that ring the hemisphere. The long wave troughs are caused by large masses of cold air, and the ridges by warm air.

Jet maxes, sometimes called jet streaks particularly when referring to smaller scales, are very important features. The winds are frequently out of balance around them, resulting in strong vertical motions. A careful isotach field that provides the correct shape of the jet streak can be very helpful in inferring areas of vertical motion.

A conceptual model exists which suggests the type of vertical motion that may exist around a jet max. It is usually referred to as the "4-cell jet max concept". The coordinate system specifies that "left" is the poleward direction, "right" is equatorward, "rear" is upstream, and "front" is downstream. Upward motion should be found in the left front quadrant (LFQ) and right rear quadrant (RRQ), with downward motion in the right front quadrant (RFQ) and left rear quadrant (LRQ). In cyclonic flow the left quadrants are enhanced with the right quadrants nullified, with the opposite true in anticyclonic flow. This concept is highly subjective and is subject to assumptions, but demonstrates an excellent use for the upper tropospheric chart.

Great sites with real-time data for this product . . .
❍ NWS DIFAX — **weather.noaa.gov/fax/nwsfax.html**
❍ UCAR — **www.rap.ucar.edu/weather/upper**
❍ College of DuPage — **weather.cod.edu/analysis**
❍ Unisys — **weather.unisys.com/upper_air**

■ The 300 mb chart is usually at a height of about 30,000 ft. The 250 mb chart is usually at a height of about 34,000 ft. The 200 mb chart is usually at a height of about 39,000 ft.

■ Upper air plots are explained in Table 1B in the Appendix.

■ Warm pockets at 200 mb may be an indicator of strong upper-tropospheric divergence (ascent and bad weather).

■ **Fields**
- Height contours are drawn as solid black lines every 120 m (12 dam) using 900 dam as a base value (888, 900, 912, etc). Labels are in dam.
- Isotachs are drawn as purple lines every 20 kt starting at 30 kt as a base (30, 50, 70, 90, etc).
- Isotherms (optional) are dashed red lines every 5 C°, but may clutter the chart.

■ **Features**
- High and low height centers are plotted as a large black "H" or "L", with the decameter value below it.
- Jet axes. The axis of jets should be drawn as a heavy red arrow. Col. Robert Miller's Severe Weather Analysis Notes suggests a purple color for this level.
- Jet cores. Draw a red ellipse to mark the jet core.

■ Isotach bands can be shaded using colored pencils.
- One possible shading spectrum is green to yellow to red.
- The Environment Canada scheme is:

- 60-90 kt	Green
- 90-120 kt	Red
- 120-150 kt	Blue
- 150-180 kt	Purple
- 181+ kt	Yellow

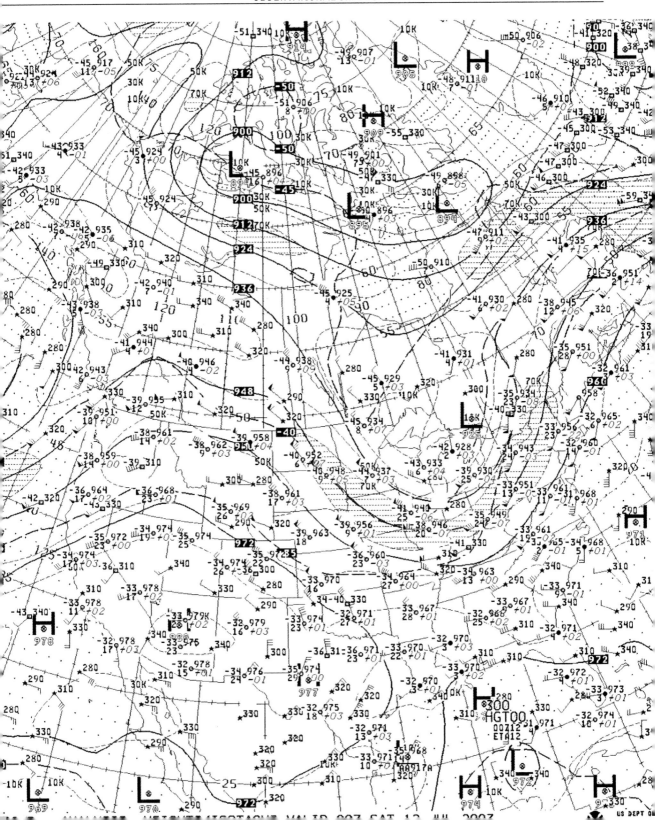

Thickness Analysis

Thickness is a direct measurement of the vertical distance between one pressure surface and another. By convention it is expressed in whole meters, or more commonly, as dekameters (tens of meters), abbreviated as "dam". Contours are usually drawn every 6 dam. Thickness is useful to forecasters because it provides an indication of the average temperature within the layer being sampled. Overall, high thickness values are always associated with warm air, while low thickness values are associated with cold air.

To be more exact, thickness measures the average *virtual temperature*, which is only slightly different from actual temperature by no more than one or two Celsius degrees. At any given virtual temperature (i.e. any given thickness) an air mass will be slightly cooler if it is humid and slightly warmer if dry.

The most common layer found in operational meteorology is the layer between 1000 and 500 mb, which yields the *1000-500 mb thickness*. This layer, which occupies the area roughly between sea level and 18,000 ft MSL, represents the bottom half of the troposphere where the majority of air mass contrasts exist. During extremely cold events that involve much more shallow air masses, the 1000-700 mb or even the 1000-850 mb thickness may be used to better define fronts and air masses. However such charts are extremely difficult to find on the Internet, and as a result are only available to those with weather display software.

Thickness plots are almost always displayed together with isobars, which connect lines of equal pressure. This provides an accurate relationship of the pressure gradient (and wind) to the thermal contrasts and air masses that exist.

Thickness charts provide one of the most reliable ways to assess thermal advection. Advection occurs where wind is blowing colder or warmer thicknesses into a given location. Where "boxes" are painted out by the isobars and thickness lines, it implies that either warm or cold advection is taking place.

Specific thickness lines have been used for decades to highlight rain-snow transition areas. The most common transition line is the 540 dam line (usually ±4 dam) on the 1000-500 mb thickness chart, which correlates to the rough location of rain-snow transition at sea level. The corresponding line on the 1000-700 mb chart is 284 dam and on the 1000-850 mb chart it is 130 dam.

Great sites with real-time data for this product . . .
- NWS DIFAX — **weather.noaa.gov/fax/nwsfax.html**
- College of DuPage — **weather.cod.edu/forecast**
- Unisys — **weather.unisys.com/eta/pres.html**

■ Thickness is an indicator of average temperature through a given layer of the atmosphere, usually from 1000 to 500 mb. Thickness lines can be thought of as isotherms for the entire layer. Thickness charts are used to locate fronts, air masses, and areas of thermal advection.

■ This product is often found only as a "model derived" product with surface sea-level pressure (SLP) progs.

■ Low thickness corresponds to cold air. High thickness implies warm air.

■ Warm advection is associated with large-scale ascent, clouds, and rain. Cold advection is associated with subsidence and clear skies.

■ Cold fronts tend to be associated with cyclonically curved thickness lines; warm fronts are associated with anticyclonically curved thickness lines.

■ Bands of thickness lines are thermal gradients which tend to separate different air masses. A surface front usually exists on the warm edge of bands of thickness lines (thermal gradients).

■ A surface low riding along the warm side of a thickness gradient is developing or mature. When it recedes within or poleward of the thickness gradient, it is occluding.

■ When forecasting precipitation type in unfamiliar regions, you can use the 540 dam line on the 1000-500 mb thickness chart as a crude "first guess" as to where rain will transition to snow at sea level.

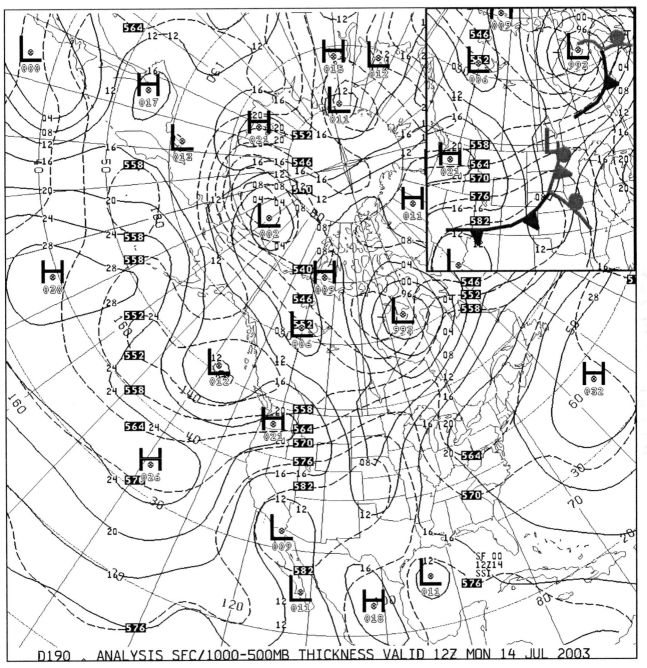

D190 ANALYSIS SFC/1000-500MB THICKNESS VALID 12Z MON 14 JUL 2003

Above: Thickness chart for the 1000-500 mb layer. Note the "boxes" formed by the juxtaposition of the thickness and pressure lines, which imply thermal advection. Strong cold advection exists over Montana and Wyoming, while strong warm advection exists over Wisconsin and Minnesota. A frontal system (inset) is suggested by the patterns. The pressure-thickness chart is an excellent tool that can be used to infer frontal systems from model output, even when surface data is not available. *(NOAA/NCEP)*

Isentropic Analysis

Isentropic analysis works on the understanding that a parcel of air does not move in a pure horizontal fashion but will cling to its own isentropic (potential temperature) surface, providing that there are no outside influences such as heating, evaporation, and condensation. Because of this, vertical motion can be easily assessed simply by looking at the slope of the isentropic surfaces and the direction of the winds along the surface.

Isentropic analysis was widely used during the 1940s and 1950s, but was largely abandoned with the first surge of model data. By 1980 it was almost forgotten. It wasn't until the early 1990s that the availability of instantaneous isentropic diagnosis on personal computers helped revive the technique. It is now in common use at most forecasting offices.

The basis of isentropic analysis is the rule that surfaces bend upward above a cold air mass and dip downward over a warm air mass. This implies that when a mid-level parcel crosses from an area of low-level warm air to a region of low-level cold air, it must rise to follow the upward bend in the isentropic surface. This is the concept of "overrunning" ascent that occurs along warm fronts. Likewise, a movement from cold to warm air suggests isentropic descent. Even winds aren't necessary if the isentropic surfaces are moving. If cold air is moving into an area of warm air, a stationary parcel must rise to adhere to its isentropic surface.

In interpreting the isentropic analysis chart, isopleths of equal height in millibars will be displayed. For example, if we are looking at a 300 K isentropic level and a isopleth marked "700" crosses Vermont, we can conclude that the 300 K surface is at the 700 mb level in Vermont. Therefore contours with low values indicate high heights, and high values indicate low heights.

The second important component of the isentropic chart is wind barbs, which are valid for that isentropic level. So if a wind barb with southwest winds at 40 kt show over Vermont in the example above, it can be concluded that this particular wind sample exists at the 700 mb level. Since the wind data is solidly linked with the isentropic surface, we can assume that given a situation where winds aloft are strong and winds near the surface are weak, that the isentropic chart will show strong winds only in areas where the height contours show high heights.

It is important to remember that isentropic analysis works best in a "dry" atmosphere with very little heating from the surface. Therefore it is usually discarded during the summer.

Great sites with real-time data for this product . . .
○ College of DuPage — **weather.cod.edu/analysis**

■ Isentropic analysis shows the conditions only along an imaginary isentropic surface, which varies greatly with height depending on the temperature of the air below it. Parcels have a tendency to follow this surface, so ascent or descent can be determined by looking at the horizontal winds along this surface.

■ Isentropic charts usually contain contours that show the height of the surface in millibars (lower values indicate larger heights) as well as winds at this level. Relative humidity is often added to visualize how close the parcels are to being saturated.

■ To see a higher elevation, choose a higher K isentropic level. To see a lower elevation, choose a lower one.

■ Use warmer (higher K) charts in the summer, and colder (lower K) charts in the winter. Cold charts tend to intersect the ground during the summer, and warm charts are too high in the winter.

■ Isentropic analysis performs poorly in the summer when convection regimes are in place. Its best performance is found on a winter night in a dry, stable frontal pattern over a flat prairie region.

Right: In this example for the 310 K surface, a ridge of lower isentropic heights (warm air) covers much of the northern Plains. A cross section from Minneapolis to Boston, parallel to the wind flow, helps visualize this chart. Note the sudden jump near Toronto, where the parcel suddenly ascends to higher heights. This is an instance of "overrunning" along a warm front. Also note how some surfaces intersect the ground.

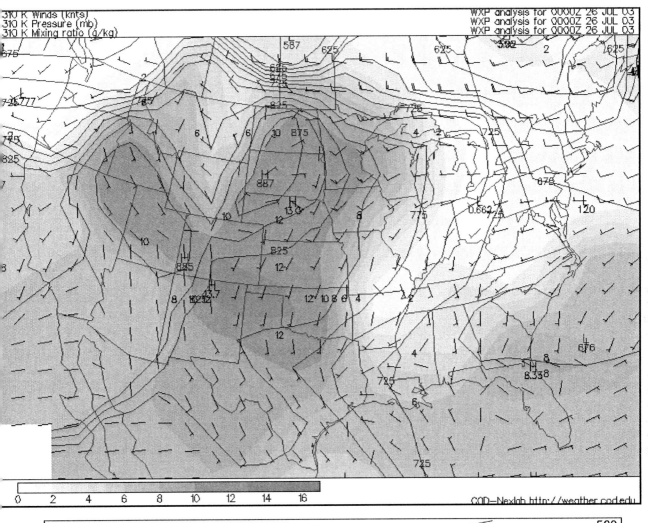

310 K Winds (knts)
310 K Pressure (mb)
310 K Mixing ratio (g/kg)

WXP analysis for 0000Z 26 JUL 03
WXP analysis for 0000Z 26 JUL 03
WXP analysis for 0000Z 26 JUL 03

COD—Nexlab http://weather.cod.edu

0   2   4   6   8   10   12   14   16

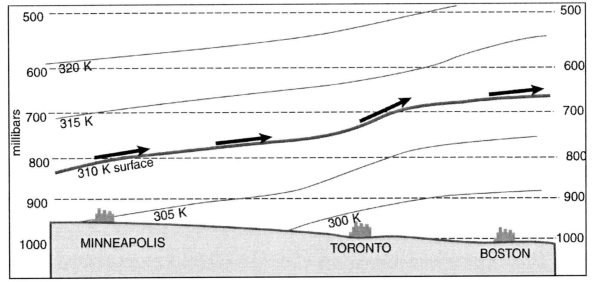

Vorticity Analysis

Vorticity is a measure of the spin of a given parcel of air. This is created by two qualities within the flow: shear and curvature. Shear is the difference in winds on opposite sides of the parcel. Curvature describes any turning path that the parcel must follow.

Consider a truck driver towing a giant carousel on a flatbed trailer. The carousel is free on its ball bearings, and any object or gust of wind causes it to spin. If the truck overtakes a slow driver in the left lane, while a fast car rushes by in the right lane, the carousel will tend to spin counter-clockwise. This represents shear. If the road bends to the left, the carousel will spin a little faster counterclockwise while it goes around the bend. The effect would be readily observable to a person watching from an airplane. This type of turning motion represents curvature.

For most conventional vorticity analysis, forecasters use a quantity called *absolute vorticity*. This is the actual spin of the parcel of air, plus the spin of the earth. Another type of vorticity called *relative vorticity* exists, which consists of pure spin and curvature, however in practice it is only used for charts close to the surface to help find small-scale cyclones.

Absolute vorticity is typically calculated by computer systems at the 500 mb (18,000 ft MSL) level. Vorticity advection occurs where wind speed is strong (height contours close together) and vorticity gradient is strong (vorticity contours close together). Therefore where the smallest "boxes" are formed by the vorticity and height contours, advection is strongest. It uses a small part of the omega equation for vertical motion to make limited assumptions about ascent or descent.

Cyclonic vorticity advection (CVA) is tied to ascent of air, which results in clouds and precipitation. On the other hand, anticyclonic vorticity advection (AVA) is associated with subsidence, which favors clear skies. In the Northern Hemisphere, CVA is the same thing as positive vorticity advection (PVA) since higher values of vorticity are being advected in, while AVA is referred to as negative vorticity advection (NVA).

The principle of tying vorticity advection to vertical motion goes on several shaky assumptions. The first is that the atmosphere is responsive to restoration of geostrophic balance. The second is that the advection rate increases with height. The third is that CVA is not negated by cold advection, or that AVA is not negated by warm advection.

Great sites with real-time data for this product . . .
○ NWS DIFAX — **weather.noaa.gov/fax/nwsfax.html**
○ College of DuPage — **weather.cod.edu/forecast**
○ Unisys — **weather.unisys.com/eta**
○ UCAR — **www.rap.ucar.edu/weather/model**
○ TTU — **www.mesonet.ttu.edu/upper_air/start.html**

■ The use of vorticity analysis for finding vertical motion involves several assumptions and should be used with extreme caution.

■ In the northern hemisphere, PVA (positive vorticity advection) is the same thing as CVA (cyclonic vorticity advection. Likewise, NVA (negative vorticity advection) is the same thing as AVA (anticyclonic vorticity advection).

■ Areas of CVA are often associated with ascent. The ascent will be enhanced if warm advection is occurring in the lower troposphere. It will be negated (or even result in subsidence) if cold advection is occurring.

■ Areas of AVA are associated with subsidence. The descent will be enhanced if cold advection is occurring in the lower troposphere. It will be negated (or even result in ascent) if warm advection is occurring.

■ Areas of strong CVA should be shaded red. Areas of strong AVA should be shaded blue.

■ If you do not feel adept at finding areas of PVA and NVA, look for the boxes formed by the cross-overlap of height and vorticity.

■ Short wave troughs are upstream from PVA areas and downstream from NVA areas. They are drawn with a thick straight line.

■ Short wave ridges are generally downstream from PVA areas and upstream from NVA areas. They are drawn with a zig-zag line.

500 mb Heights (dm) / Abs. Vorticity (x10^{-5} s^{-1})

Analysis valid 0000 UTC Tue 15 Jul 2003   Eta (00z 15 Jul)

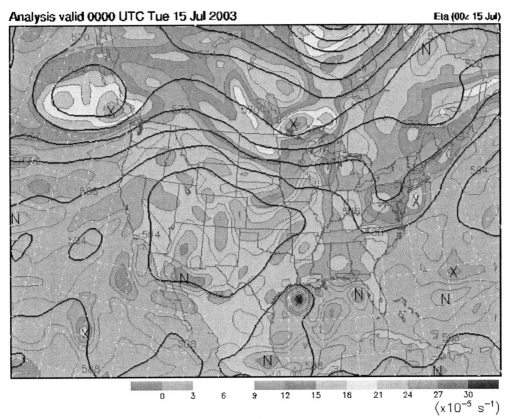

0   3   6   9   12   15   18   21   24   27   30

(x10^{-5} s^{-1})

Top: Heights (solid lines) and vorticity (patterns and shading) for 500 mb. A short wave trough, manifested by high vorticity, is along the Wisconsin coastline, with strong positive vorticity advection and implied ascent over Lake Michigan. When visiting a new site it is always important to familiarize yourself with the color scheme so that you can recognize which vorticity units are low and which are high. Many sites shade low vorticity in blue, and high vorticity in red. *(UCAR)*

Right: Analysis of basic features in a 500 mb height-vort chart for the North Pacific. The "boxes" drawn in one sample PVA area help illustrate how imaginary vorticity advection boxes are formed. The smaller the boxes, the stronger the vorticity advection. Note the predictable relationship of PVA and NVA areas between short wave troughs and ridges. *(NOAA/ NCEP)*

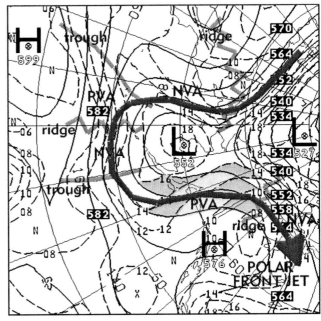

Vertical Velocity (Omega)

One meteorological parameter brings a paradox: it is perhaps one of the most important in operational forecasting, yet it cannot be directly measured. It is vertical velocity. A proxy exists for estimating vertical motion, called the quasi-geostrophic omega equation, which is able to estimate the vertical velocity indirectly using other types of measurements.

The reason that vertical velocity cannot be measured directly is partly because anemometers cannot simply be mounted sideways. The vertical motion which produces widespread areas of light rain and snow, for example, may be on the order of millimeters or centimeters per second! Any attempt to measure the quantity would be corrupted by the effects of horizontal wind and turbulence. Furthermore there are practical difficulties in siting a sensor ten or twenty thousand feet above the ground.

Omega specifies that when cyclonic vorticity increases with height and/or warm advection is present, upward motion should occur to restore geostrophic and hydrostatic balance. The amount of each quantity is proportional to the vertical motion. Omega is expressed in microbars per second of vertical motion, with a microbar being a thousandth of a millibar. One microbar per second in the low levels is roughly one centimeter per second of ascent or subsidence. A *positive value indicates subsidence*, while a *negative value indicates ascent*.

At first glance omega appears to deliver the prized vertical motion values that all forecasters seek. However a closer look reveals serious caveats. First, accurately measuring and gauging the data and applying them to a meteorologically representative field is not as easy as it seems. Consider that a numerical analysis gridpoint can represent the observation at either Albany, Buffalo, or a weighted combination of the two. Different objective analysis techniques can produce slightly different values at the gridpoint. Any discrepancy from an "ideal" value for the gridpoint, given the starting conditions, can amplify into large errors when the model goes forth with calculations to determine omega. Even initial numerical weather prediction panels can start with a significant amount of omega "noise" due to aberrations in the analyzed temperature and wind fields.

Furthermore the vorticity parameter and thermal advection parameter often negate each other, which reduces the magnitude of vertical motion to such a small scale that the spectre of uncertainty overshadows the results. This has serious implications considering the difficulty in obtaining a properly balanced initialization in the model run.

■ Omega is equal to dp/dt (the change in pressure of a parcel over a given time), and is expressed in microbars per second.

■ By its definition, negative values indicate ascent and positive values indicate subsidence.

■ One microbar per second equals one centimeter per second. For the aviation-oriented, this equals 1.97 feet per minute. This is only a very rough approximation for the lower troposphere.

■ Some typical values of lift in microbars per second. Convective speeds are provided only for comparision; model omega only accounts for large-scale ascent and does not factor in convection.

Speed	Weather
0.5	Stratus
5	Light rain
50	Heavy rain, cumulus
500	Thunderstorm
5000	Tornadic thunderstorm

■ Some websites and graphics packages may reverse the sign of omega. Always inspect the fields carefully before you use a new site.

■ Moisture is needed before ascent can produce either clouds or precipitation. The higher the relative humidity, the more probable this will occur.

Great sites with real-time data for this product . . .
❍ College of DuPage — **weather.cod.edu/forecast**
❍ Unisys — **weather.unisys.com/ngm**

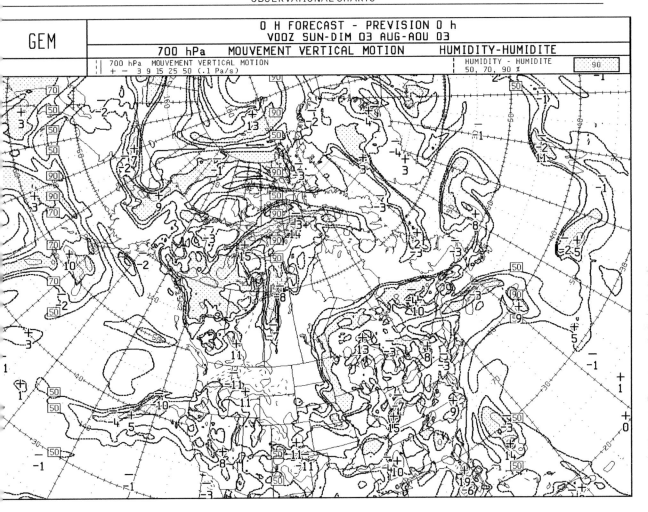

GEM

0 H FORECAST - PREVISION 0 h
V00Z SUN-DIM 03 AUG-AOU 03
700 hPa   MOUVEMENT VERTICAL MOTION   HUMIDITY-HUMIDITE

700 hPa   MOUVEMENT VERTICAL MOTION
+ −   3 9 15 25 50 (.1 Pa/s)

HUMIDITY - HUMIDITE
50, 70, 90 %

90

Top: 700 mb vertical velocity (omega) product from the Meteorological Service of Canada, as output from the initial panel of their GEM/Regional run. *(CMC)*

Right: 700 mb vertical velocity (omega) product from the RUC run, as obtained at College of DuPage's Nexlab. Omega fields are often noisy, especially in convective weather regimes and during the evening hours. *(College of DuPage)*

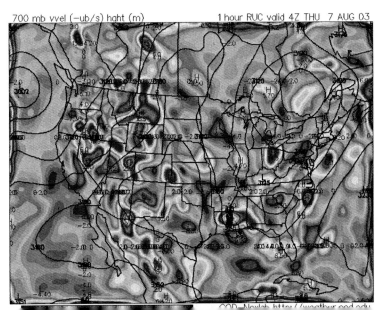

700 mb vvel (−ub/s) hght (m)   1 hour RUC valid 4Z THU 7 AUG 03

Q Vector Analysis

Q vector is a diagnostic product, with Q representing the term "quasi-geostrophic". A Q vector is an imaginary value that is equal to the rate of change of the horizontal potential temperature gradient. It gives an idea of the type of flow that must develop for the thermal wind balance to be maintained. This may consist of convergence, divergence, and most importantly, vertical motion.

The Q vector technique is rather new, dating back to 1978 in a paper published by British meteorologists Brian Hoskins, Ion Draghici, and Huw Davies. It was later advanced in the United States during the 1980s by analysis expert Stanley Barnes, and by the 1990s had gained widespread acceptance as one of many tools to diagnose vertical motion.

Looking at one Q vector by itself, whenever its magnitude is high, a strong horizontal ageostrophic wind is implied. This is interpreted as a response by the atmosphere to restore the thermal wind balance. Vertical motion is likely to develop to compensate for the imbalance when the Q vectors are convergent or divergent.

In a convergent pattern, the Q vectors tend to point at one another. This implies ascent at that level. In a divergent pattern, the Q vectors point away from one another. This implies subsidence at that level. Some panels and software displays are able to directly measure the magnitude of convergence or divergence, eliminating much of the guesswork. The result immediately suggests the sign and the intensity of the implied ascent or descent.

Also, Q vectors are often overlaid on top of a product showing isotherms for that level, or thickness for a layer centered on that level. This reveals important information about whether the thermal boundaries and fronts are strengthening or weakening. When Q vectors point from cold to warm air, the thermal gradient is strengthening and frontogenesis is implied. When Q vectors point from warm to cold air, the thermal gradient is weakening and frontolysis (weakening of a front) is implied.

Going a step further, the thickness gradient pattern has been shown to have some bearing on the surface pressure patterns. Where the thermal gradient is showing an "S" shape and Q vectors indicate frontogenesis, cyclogenesis is implied, with falling surface pressures and deteriorating weather.

Great sites with real-time data for this product . . .
○ TTU — **www.mesonet.ttu.edu/upper_air/start.html**
○ U of W — **speedy.meteor.wisc.edu/~swetzel/winter/**

■ A Q vector with a high magnitude indicates strongly ageostrophic flow.

■ Q vector convergence is associated with ascent.

■ Q vector divergence is associated with subsidence.

■ Q vectors pointing from cold to warm air indicate frontogenesis.

■ Q vectors pointing from warm to cold air indicate frontolysis.

■ Q vectors pointing parallel to isotherms or thickness lines suggest prounounced thermal advection is occurring.

■ Qs vector is the component parallel to the thermal contours, useful for measuring advection. Qn vector is the component perpendicular to the contours, which measures frontogenesis or frontolysis.

■ According to Lance Bosart at SUNY, high-resolution model fields (particularly less than 40 km) are too noisy and unbalanced to accurately calculate a Q vector. It may be best to use smoothed fields, particularly the 1-deg AVN grid. The 80-km resolution model output and especially layer Q vectors are commonly regarded as giving the best results.

■ Layer Q vectors are preferred over single-level Q vectors. This is because they smooth out noise, which can seriously degrade the value of the product.

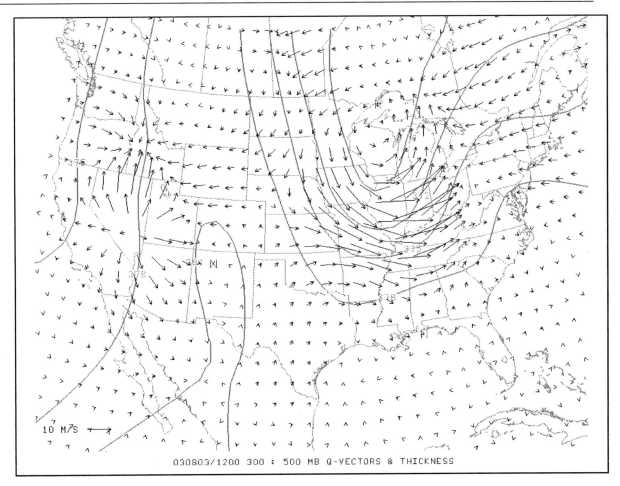

030803/1200 300 : 500 MB Q-VECTORS & THICKNESS

Top: Q vector analysis as obtained from Texas Tech University (TTU). This layer shows the 300-500 mb layer. The TTU charts stand out among a vacuum of Q-vector products on the Internet. *(TTU)*

Right: A companion field available on the TTU site actually measures the Q-vector divergence (dashed lines with no shading) and convergence (colored shading). The thick concentric lines centered on Kansas indicate the layer isotachs, which were actually errone-ous on this frame due to a bad obser-vation at Dodge City, contaminating the entire field in the central United States. *(TTU)*

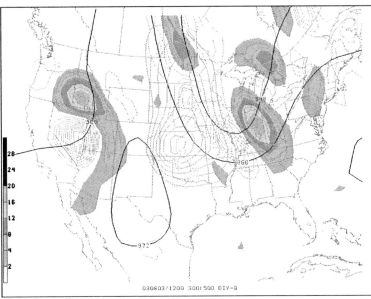

030803/1200 300:500 DIV-Q

Thermodynamic Diagram
(Sounding, SKEW-T, etc)

The thermodynamic diagram shows the change of the temperature and dewpoint above a given weather station with height. The X-coordinate is always temperature, and the Y-coordinate is height. However, the temperature coordinates are skewed 45 degrees to the right to help make important contrasts stand out better. Using these coordinates, observations of temperature and dewpoint at various heights are plotted. Since dewpoint is always equal to or lower than temperature, the dewpoint trace is usually to the left of the temperature trace. It is typically shown as a dashed rather than a solid line.

The most important use of the sounding is to assess the degree of instability present in the atmosphere. If any part of the sounding leans sharply to the left with height, it is assumed to have a large lapse rate (a great temperature decrease with height). If the dewpoint trace indicates significant moisture at the surface, the moisture and its potential for latent heat release will combine with this large lapse rate to produce an unstable atmosphere.

The simplest measure of instability is the Showalter Stability Index (SSI) and the Lifted Index (LI). However, both of these rely on a simple comparision of the parcel with the environment at one level. A far more accurate measure is Convective Availability of Potential Energy (CAPE), which assesses the parcel-environment temperature differential throughout the entire vertical column. A CAPE value should always be used except when it is not available. All instability calculations depend on an accurate representation of parcel temperature and moisture, which in turn requires a representative integration of low-level moisture and an accurate temperature forecast. Human manipulation of the parcel attributes are always worthwhile, and are easy to do on paper SKEW-T diagrams and in certain weather software applications.

The basic concept for determining the type of precipitation that reaches the surface is to begin in the mid-levels of the troposphere, determine what type of precipitation it begins as, and observe the temperature regimes that affect the particle as it falls downward. As a rule of thumb, 1200 ft of warm air is considered ample to completely melt snow, with 400 ft of cold air considered enough to freeze liquid precipitation.

Great sites with real-time data for this product . . .
- UCAR — **www.rap.ucar.edu/weather/upper**
- Unisys — **weather.unisys.com/upper_air/skew**
- College of DuPage — **weather.cod.edu/analysis**
- U of Wyo. — **weather.uwyo.edu/upperair/sounding.html**

■ Height lines are horizontal and are usually calibrated in millibars. The top of the chart is usually 100 mb (about 53,000 ft) and the bottom is usually 1050 mb (about minus 300 ft MSL).

■ Temperature lines slope up and to the right. They are calibrated in degrees Celsius with an interval of every 10 C°.

■ Dry adiabats slope up and to the left. These indicate how a dry parcel will cool as it rises.

■ Moist (wet) adiabats slope upward and then curve sharply to the left. These indicate how a saturated parcel will cool as it rises.

■ Mixing ratio lines slope upward and to the right. They are more vertical than the temperature lines, and are typically omitted in the upper portion of the sounding. A rising parcel's dewpoint will follow these lines upward until it saturates.

■ The thermodynamic diagram has dozens of uses that are impossible to fully summarize in this guide.

■ A software package dedicated to working with soundings is highly recommended and makes quick, accurate work of parcel estimates and daytime heating influences. RAOB (*www.weathergraphics.com/raob*) is currently the only fully capable Windows sounding program.

■ The "bible" for the SKEW-T is "The Use of the Skew-T Log-P Diagram in Analysis and Forecasting" by Robert C. Miller, AWS TR-200.

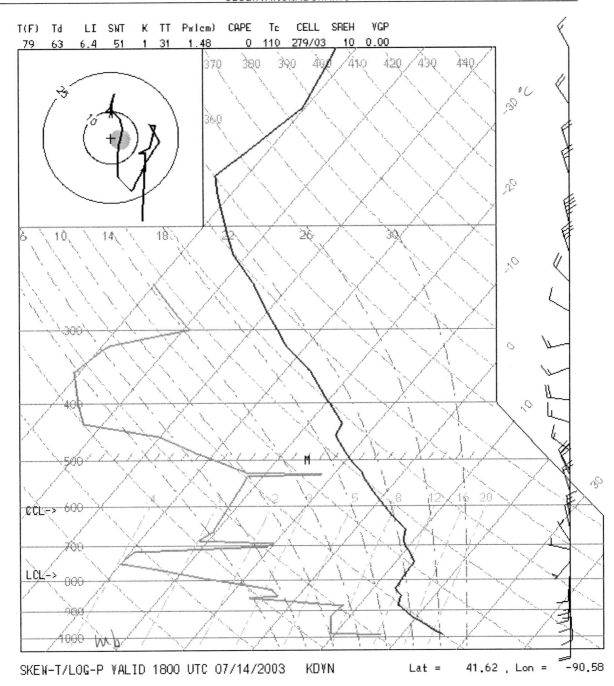

T(F)	Td	LI	SWT	K	TT	Pw(cm)	CAPE	Tc	CELL	SREH	VGP
79	63	6.4	51	1	31	1.48	0	110	279/03	10	0.00

SKEW-T/LOG-P VALID 1800 UTC 07/14/2003   KDVN   Lat =   41.62 , Lon =   -90.58

Above: Sounding for Davenport, Iowa. An inversion exists between 750 and 825 mb. The layer just above the surface is superadiabatic, which suggests either a minor sensor problem or a very unusual atmospheric occurrence. *(UCAR)*

Wind Profilers

A wind profiler is a special type of Doppler radar that measures wind speed with a fixed antenna. The radar is able to project in two perpendicular locations off the vertical axis in order to measure the horizontal wind components. The advantage of a wind profiler is that it can sample winds continuously without the need for as many scatterers as needed by a WSR-88D producing a VAD/VWP product, and they have fewer moving parts and thus are less capable of breaking down.

Profilers typically operate in a high mode and a low mode. The low mode usually covers the lower and middle troposphere (up to about 9 km), while the high mode covers the upper troposphere (from about 7 to 16 km) in a much more sensitive detection mode.

A piggyback technology incorporated in most soundings is called Radio Acoustic Sounding System (RASS). Its main function is to estimate temperature at various layers. Since the speed of sound is dependent on temperature, RASS allows temperature to be measured. A 900 Hz burst of acoustic sound is transmitted upward into the atmosphere and is measured. The reliability of data from this technology is not quite clear yet.

A special type of wind profiler is called Sonic Detection and Ranging (SODAR). It relies entirely on acoustic echoes for detecting wind speed, and its vertical limit of about 1000 ft confines it to research and other special applications.

Unfortunately in June 2003 it was announced that wind profilers were to be cut from the United States FY2004 budget, and ironically with the full endorsement of National Oceanic and Atmospheric Administration officials. The 35 sites, installed at a cost of $20 million during the early 1990s, carry a $4.15 million maintenance cost. They contributed greatly to severe storm forecasting on the Great Plains, including the success of the 3 May 1999 tornado forecasts in centralOklahoma. The move will provide less data for new mesoscale models.

Europe has continued to invest in wind profiler technology and currently maintains a network of about 26 wind profilers stretching from northern Italy and Spain to Germany, the United Kingdom, and Norway. The data is available on the Internet without restriction at the UK Met Office website <www.metoffice.gov.uk/research/interproj/cwinde/profiler>.

Great sites with real-time data for this product . . .
○ FSL — **www.profiler.noaa.gov/jsp/profiler.jsp**
○ UCAR — **www.rap.ucar.edu/weather/upper/**
○ College of DuPage — **weather.cod.edu/analysis**
○ UK Met Office — **http://www.met-office.gov.uk/research/interproj/cwinde/profiler/**

■ Wind profilers are a special type of clear-air Doppler radar with no moving parts. They often come with RASS units which measure temperature by projecting acoustic beeps toward the zenith.

■ Wind profilers usually require six minutes for each cycle. This is comprised of three 2-minute samples: one at the zenith, one tilted in the X direction, and one tilted in the Y direction. Within each of these modes, there is a 1-minute sample in low mode and another in high mode (see text).

■ The NOAA 404 MHz wind profilers are programmed to shut down when SARSAT search and rescue satellites pass overhead, in order to avoid interfering with their sensors which operate on a similar frequency. This inhibit mode occurs about 4 to 10 times per day, and lasts for about six minutes. It will cause a gap in the observations. The NOAA FSL Profiler site maintains a list of scheduled inhibit times.

■ Strips of bad data may be caused by aircraft flying over the profiler.

■ Most wind profilers in the United States may be unplugged by 2004 due to NOAA budget cuts.

■ When checking a profiler plot at a new Web site, always remember to check the scale at the bottom to see which side has the most current plot. There is no standard scheme.

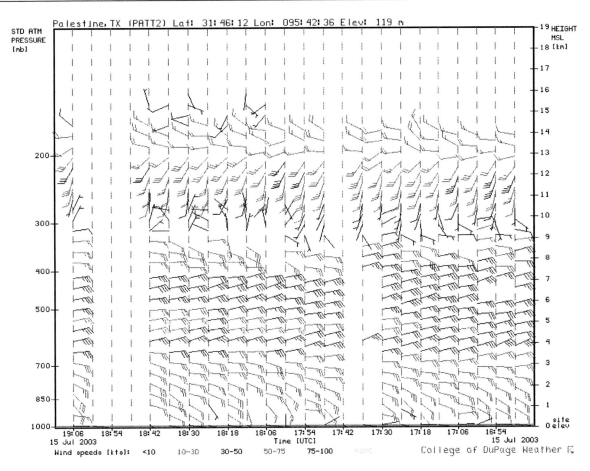

Above: Typical profile plot for one site. The coordinates are reversed time (X-axis) and height (Y-axis). The newest plot is on the left side. Using this plot it is easy to see the wind direction and speed at any given level above the station.

Right: An excellent use of the profiler plot is a horizontal plot of multiple stations. In this case the 3 km winds are selected. Unfortunately, coverage is not nationwide, as most profilers are installed in the central United States.

(All products from the College of DuPage weather site at weather.cod.edu)

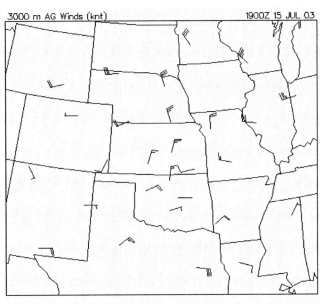

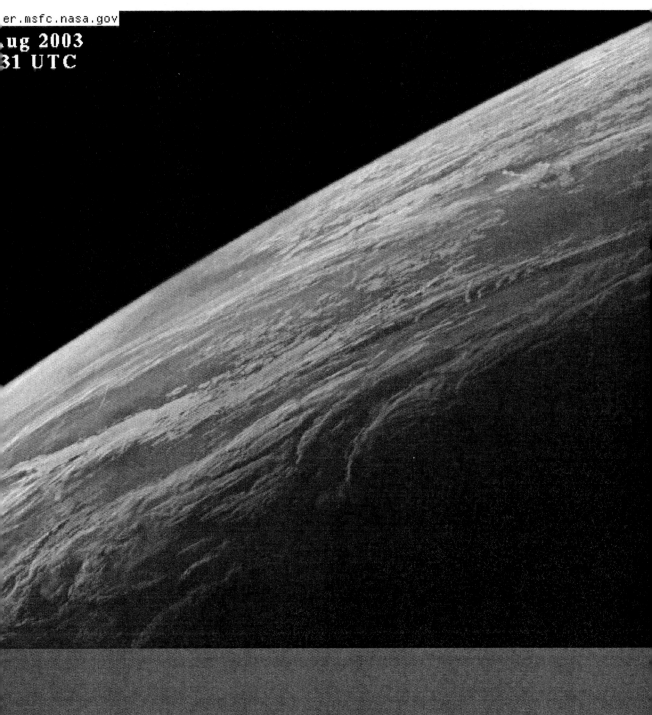

er.msfc.nasa.gov

ug 2003
31 UTC

SATELLITE

Above: Even weather satellites can capture ethereal beauty. This zoomed view shows August sunset over northern British Columbia and Yukon (top). *(NASA/GSFC)*

Satellite

In April 1960, the world's first weather satellite was launched, named TIROS (Television InfraRed Observation Satellite). Those were basically television cameras mounted on small orbiting platforms. It was only during the 1970s when satellite technology began reaching today's levels of sophistication. And finally in the mid-1990s, detailed satellite imagery became available freely to anyone who had access to the Internet.

Weather satellite imagery consists of visible, infrared, and water vapor imagery. There are also complex multispectral products available. Each will be covered in the sections ahead. However right now we will take a look at the major classes of weather satellites: geostationary and low-orbiting.

Geostationary earth orbiting (GEO)

Geostationary satellites are placed in orbit 19,312 nm above the Earth's surface. At this altitude their west-to-east motion equals that of the Earth's surface, so they are permanently "locked" onto whichever meridian they are poised above. The imager scans the Earth in a raster format, using the spacecraft's spin for imaging along one axis and a stepping mirror for incrementing the imager along the perpendicular axis. This allows the spacecraft to build an image with a minimum of moving parts.

The first geostationary satellite was ATS-1, launched in December 1966. The first of the GOES-class satellites was SMS-1, launched on May 5, 1974 and operational from 1974 to 1981. It was initially a NASA project, but since then the program has been largely turned over to the National Oceanic and Atmospheric Administration (NOAA). At least a dozen geostationary satellites have been launched by the United States, and are referred to as GOES (Geostationary Operational Environment Satellites).

Japan and Europe both launched their first geostationary weather satellites in 1977, maintaining consistent reliable coverage ever since. The Japanese satellite is known as GMS, while the European satellite is called METEOSAT. India, Russia, and China have also launched geostationary weather satellites with varying degrees of success and failure.

Low Earth orbiting (LEO)

The term "low-Earth orbiting" is a name given to weather satellites which orbit only about 500 miles above the ground. They are often called polar orbiters. A rotation is completed about once every 1.5 hours, and the

Below: One of the first TIROS images: May 1960, showing severe thunderstorms over Missouri. Satellite imagery has since advanced by incredible leaps. *(NOAA)*

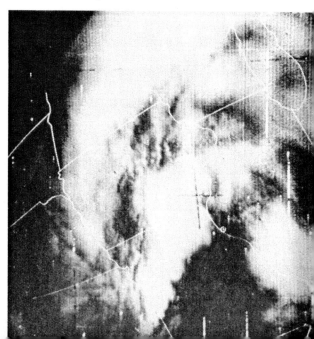

orbit is sun-synchronous, which means that it never changes when seen from a sun-relative coordinate system. The Earth's rotation allows different areas of the Earth to sweep by underneath. Also, polar orbiters often have an inclination that takes them over polar regions, giving them unmatchable ability to image regions such as Alaska, northern Canadia, Scandinavia, Russia, and Antarctica, all of which are seen at too much of a slant on GOES satellites to give useful images.

Nearly two dozen civilian LEO satellites have been launched by the U.S. government. They are referred to as the POES (Polar Orbiter Environmental Satellite) series, and are comprised of satellites designated "NOAA" (older ones were known as TIROS). The U.S. military also operates a network of LEO weather satellites known as DMSP (Defense Meteorological Satellite Program), however the imagery is encrypted and is shared with the public only through special research programs.

A highly useful series of Chinese satellites are also in orbit, referred to as FY (Fengyun), which makes up for the gap left by the Russian METEOR series, which ceased operating. Fengyun also refers to a geostationary satellite operated by China.

There are few differences in LEO satellite imagery compared to geostationary images, except that images are available much more sporadically, depending on when a satellite pass is available. Georeferencing (adding borders and geography) is considerably more complex for the ground station, and the images are always distorted due to the low-altitude view offered by the satellite. One more significant difference is that the NOAA series has much better infrared resolution than that onboard the GOES satellite.

Imagery on the Web

Most real-time satellite photos available on the Internet are of very high quality resolution, and available almost anywhere in the world. From the GOES satellites, North America

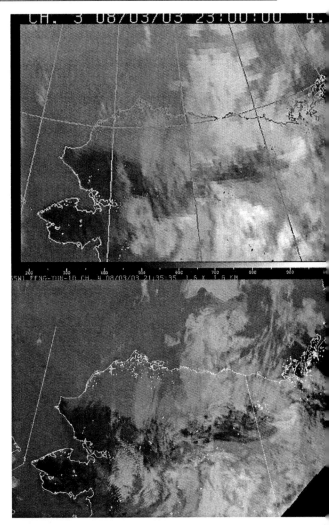

Above: Highest possible infrared resolution for GOES-10 geostationary satellite (top) compared to equivalent Chinese Feng-Yun 10 polar orbiter (bottom). The degradation in the GOES imagery caused by slant, combined with the 4 km infrared resolution in GOES compared to the 1 to 2 km packages in the polar orbiters, makes polar orbiters a staple for polar forecasting. *(NOAA/ARH)*

receives 1-km resolution visible imagery every 5 to 15 minutes; 4 km infrared imagery every 15 minutes; and 8 km water vapor imagery every 15 minutes. This is helped only by 1 km infrared imagery by low-Earth orbit satellites.

Elsewhere, hobbyists and some weather consulting firms in Europe and Asia are heavily stifled by 4 km or 8 km resolution barriers imposed by the owners of the METEOSAT and GMS satellites. This leaves a very limited assortment of satellite data to choose from, with poor suitability for mesoscale purposes. Polar orbiter data from the United States, China, and Russia provides important supplementary images.

An excellent directory of real-time data is at <www.nwas.org/committees/rs/nwasat.html>. For a selection of images for Alaska that includes POES and FY imagery, see <www.arh.noaa.gov>. Official websites for government weather satellite programs include <www.goes.noaa.gov>, <poes.gsfc.nasa.gov>, <smis.iki.rssi.ru>, <www.eumetsat.de>, <mscweb.kishou.go.jp> and <www.imd.ernet.in>.

Right: First full-disk image from the GOES series of satellites. This image was taken in October 1975 from GOES-1. NASA had operated the ATS and SMS demonstrator series over a period of nearly ten years before this date, but the GOES satellite series marks the first of a series of satellites designed especially for NOAA. *(NOAA)*

Below: The world's first geostationary satellite image. Dating back to 11 December 1966, this image was taken by ATS-1, a satellite operated by NASA. This satellite was used to relay color television and White House communications across the continent. Early weather satellite technology was largely hindered by a lack of suitable display technology at each field office. Television screens were far too coarse, high-definition computer monitors were still 15 years away, and laser printers would not be invented until 1975. Therefore film recorders were a mainstay in the early years. Quality and economy were not impressive. *(NOAA)*

GOES-1 DPT   298 1645Z   25 OCT. 75

Visible Imagery

Visible satellite imagery is the most intuitive type of satellite imagery, as it detects exactly what an astronaut would see from space. Visible imagery measures "brightness", which is a function of illumination and albedo. Albedo is the percentage of incoming sunlight which is reflected into space. Clouds composed of water droplets have a much higher albedo than ice crystal clouds.

There are several important concepts to remember when analyzing visible satellite imagery.

☐ Visible imagery is not available at night. The military DMSP satellite offers night-vision visible imagery if moonlight is available, however these are generally not distributed.

☐ Cloud type can be easily assessed, which yields considerable qualitative information on the state of air masses in a forecast region.

☐ Visible imagery is rarely used on television weathercasts, which in recent years have begun leaning heavily toward processed products. Infrared imagery offers 24-hour consistency.

☐ Wind direction in the low levels can be determined simply by looking at the alignment of cumulus fields.

☐ Dust plumes can be detected.

☐ Benign or subtle low-level boundaries, such as cold fronts and thunderstorm outflow boundaries, are readily seen on visible imagery. Such boundaries are rarely detectable on infrared imagery due to their coarser resolution; at night, radar is the second best tool.

ALBEDO VALUES

Albedo	Weather objects	Ground cover
100%	—	—
90%	Thunderstorm	—
80%	Thunderstorm	Fresh snow cover
70%	Cumulus	—
60%	Stratus	White Sands NM
50%	Thin stratus	Melting snow, salt flats
40%	Cirrus	Dry sandy soil
30%	Thin cirrostratus	Clay soil, granite, glaciers
20%	Smoke	Tundra, bare soil
10%	—	Oceans, lakes, forest
0%	(black body)	(black body)

Great sites with real-time data for this product . . .
○ NASA/GHCC — **wwwghcc.msfc.nasa.gov/GOES**
○ UCAR — **www.rap.ucar.edu/weather/satellite**
○ SSEC — **www.ssec.wisc.edu/data**
○ College of DuPage — **weather.cod.edu/analysis**
○ Universität Ulm — **meteosat.e-technik.uni-ulm.de**

■ GOES visible imagery has a resolution of 1 km, as does polar orbiter AVHRR imagery.

■ Polar orbiter AVHRR visible imagery has a resolution of 1 km and is provided on data channel 1. Channel 2 is a near-infrared channel.

■ Visible imagery is sensed in the 0.52 to 0.72 micron range, which is the green-red portion of the color spectrum.

■ The United States is probably the only country that releases its 1 km geostationary imagery for public consumption. Other countries, unfortunately, withhold their data as a value-added product for commercial sale. What is usually found is typically remapped, low-resolution sectors. For these areas, you can benefit greatly from United States and Russian polar orbiter imagery, such as NOAA-12, which covers the entire globe. The only catch is there must be a participating ground station within a line of sight to the satellite, and of course it must upload the image to the Internet.

■ You may see sun glint in the tropics, which is a spot where the majority of sunlight is reflected directly toward the satellite.

Right: GOES-12 1-km visible image for a warm summer day. Most prominent are the streets of cumulus clouds, revealing a south-to-north wind with anticyclonic curvature. Showers have formed along the Gulf Coast as a sea breeze works its way inland, casting off plumes of cirrus. *(NASA Global Hydrology and Climate Center)*

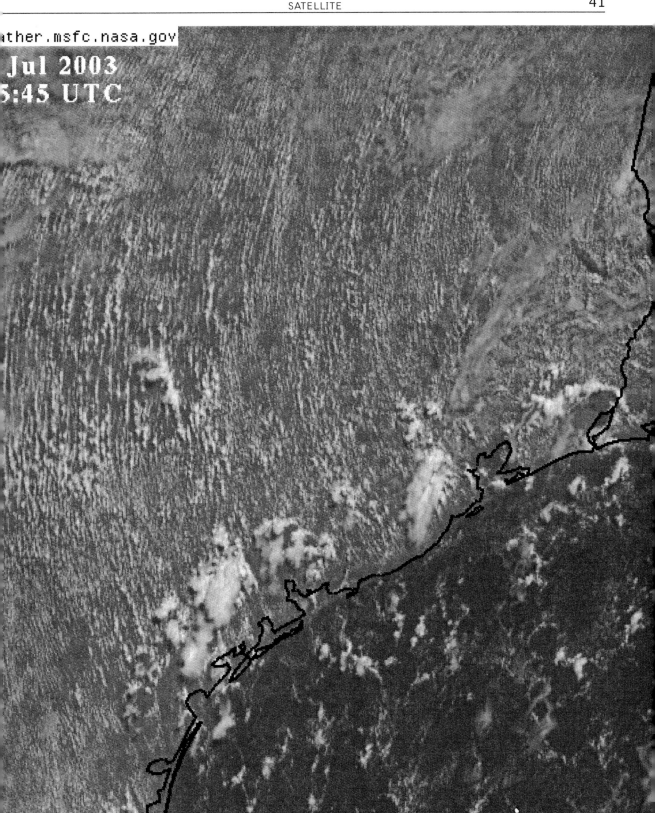

ather.msfc.nasa.gov

Jul 2003
5:45 UTC

Visible Imagery

Below: GOES-12 1-km visible image of Hurricane Claudette as it moves inland. Note that due to the sheer extent of outflow cirrus that the visible imagery helps little. The infrared imagery (q.v.) should be selected. *(College of DuPage)*

Visible Imagery Cloud Types

Compare with equivalent imagery in Infrared Imagery section

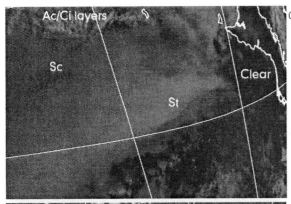

Stratus and fog appear as greyish smooth textures, with stratocumulus broken up into tiny closed or open cells. This example shows stratus off the Baja California coast, with closed-cell stratocumulus at the top left where there is slightly more instability. Stratus and fog are nearly indistinguishable, except for the fact that fog hugs surface features much more closely, particularly in river valleys. *(NOAA-14 1-km polar orbiter image; 19 July 2003 1522 UTC)*

Cumulus takes on an unmistakable speckled appearance on visible satellite imagery. In very unstable conditions or near sources of lift, they are often associated with cumulonimbus clouds, which are much larger and typically produce a fibrous cirriform anvil that may appear blotchy (with new convection) and wispy (with old convection). Compare with the equivalent infrared image in the Infrared Imagery section. *(NOAA-14 1-km polar orbiter image; 22 July 2003 2033 UTC)*

Altocumulus generally combines visual characteristics of cirrus, cumulus, and stratocumulus, as it shares common mechanisms. Shown here are altocumulus layers over the Yukon Territories, which are the debris of daytime convection. Lingering cumulus appears as sharply brighter cellular elements. *(NOAA-14 1-km polar orbiter image; 24 July 2003 0000 UTC)*

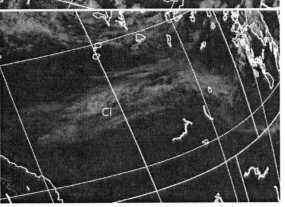

Cirrus shares a very similar appearance to its signature on infrared imagery. Because of its very strong temperature contrast with the ground, thin cirrus patches and cirrostratus sheets may show up strongly on infrared imagery but faintly on visible imagery. This cirrus patch originated from the previous evening's thunderstorms along the Canadian Rockies. *(NOAA-14 1-km polar orbiter image; 19 July 2003 1522 UTC)*

Infrared Imagery

Infrared imagery looks a lot like visible imagery, but it is actually temperature we are seeing. Dark areas correspond to areas of high thermal radiation, while white areas indicate areas of low thermal radiation. Therefore anything dark is warm, and anything white is cold. In fact, since infrared imagery helps to measure emitted radiation, it is possible to use a scale to find the temperature of any pixel in an image! For decades, weather offices in citrus farming districts have even looked for specific color ranges which match the value for freezing temperatures.

Infrared imagery is often enhanced, which refers to the technique of adding false color banding to allow certain temperature ranges to stand out. One of the most famous enhancement schemes is the MB curve, which was used by the National Weather Service for decades and highlights temperatures below minus 32°C. Various Internet sites may implement their own enhancement schemes, which may or may not be standardized, but many enhancement schemes including the example at right use a derivation of the MB curve.

Infrared satellite imagery from the GOES satellites is no better than 4 km in resolution. As most visible satellite imagery uses 1 km resolution, this means that there is usually only one infrared pixel for every 16 visible pixels. Therefore in many cases it is better to use visible imagery when available. The exception is polar orbiter imagery, which can image infrared at 1 km resolution. These can be used for case studies and special weather events when the best possible infrared imagery is needed.

Clouds may be invisible on infrared imagery when they take on the same temperature as the ground. This is true of fog; the full extent of fog is often not known until the morning hours when visible imagery is available. Stratus can often be invisible when the ground is cooler than normal. A technique that forecasters often use is to monitor whether lake surfaces, which are warmer, remain visible. A warm lake that "disappears" indicates that it has been obscured by a cloud layer.

Circular, bubble-like forms with extremely cold signatures are usually convective showers and thunderstorms. They are some of the most prominent objects, even on the crudest infrared photos.

Great sites with real-time data for this product . . .
○ NASA/GHCC — **wwwghcc.msfc.nasa.gov/GOES**
○ UCAR — **www.rap.ucar.edu/weather/satellite**
○ SSEC — **www.ssec.wisc.edu/data**
○ College of DuPage — **weather.cod.edu/analysis**
○ Universität Ulm — **meteosat.e-technik.uni-ulm.de**

■ GOES infrared imagery has a resolution of 4 km and operates on a wavelength of 11 microns.

■ Polar orbiter AVHRR infrared imagery has a resolution of 1 km (much better than GOES) and is provided on data channel 3 (short-wave) and 4 (longwave). Channel 2 is a near-infrared channel.

■ Use infrared imagery to monitor the progress of areas of upper lift.

■ During arctic air mass outbreaks, the temperatures in the northern United States and Canada can be so cold that at first glance, the infrared imagery seems to show a broad sheet of cirrostratus. You may mistake cirrostratus for the ground, or may be unable to identify any clouds whatsoever.

■ Near infrared imagery (near IR) is a special type of infrared imagery that uses the 3.9 micron band. It shares a lot in common with visible imagery and is used to differentiate low-level features that are often masked, such as snow, fog, and stratus.

Right: If you could have only one tool to summarize the weather across a region, infrared imagery could be it. The swirls and patterns shown here paint out a possible front over the northern Plains, cyclonic flow over western Ontario, a "tropical connection" over Texas, and a disorganized summertime pattern across the southeast states. *(Image from UCAR at rap.ucar.edu)*

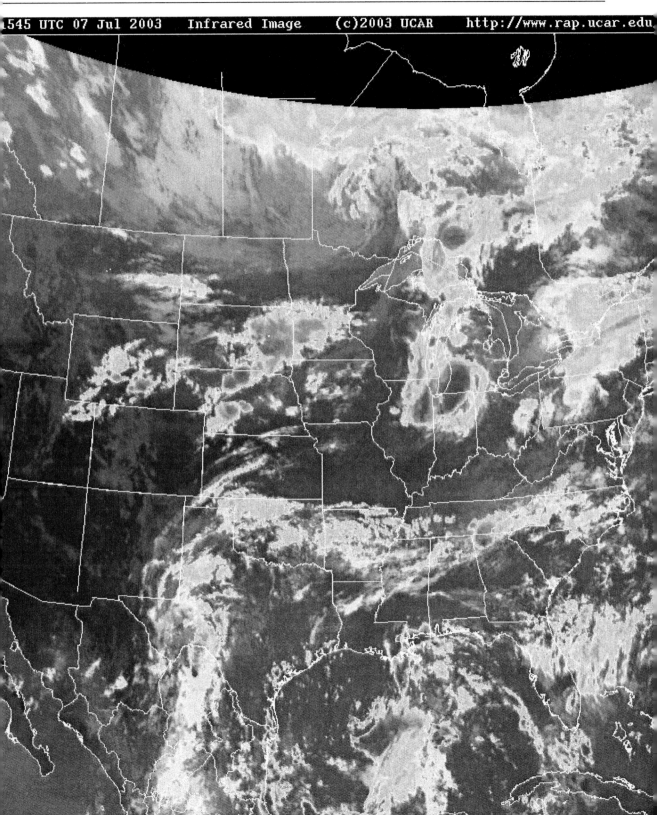

1545 UTC 07 Jul 2003   Infrared Image   (c)2003 UCAR   http://www.rap.ucar.edu

Infrared Imagery

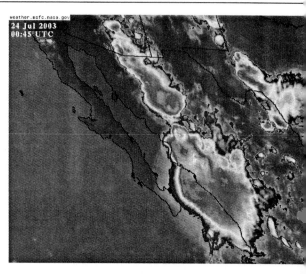

Right: Thunderstorms are a fine sight when observed on infrared satellite imagery! These massive tropical thunderstorms, with tops estimated at 60,000 ft, have fired in a common area in July: in the Mexican mountains adjacent to the Gulf of California. This daily fountain of moisture throughout all levels of the troposphere eventually works its way north in to Arizona, supplying fuel for the Mexican monsoon storms that affect Tucson and Phoenix.

Below: To enhance or not to enhance? Enhancement can help convective elements and important cloud structures stand out. For a hurricane, as shown below, this can be vital when radar is not available. However unenhanced satellite imagery can help remove some of the artificial clutter. The hurricane eye, for example, may reveal some characteristics that would otherwise be obscured on the enhanced image. *(Sample images on this page obtained from the excellent NASA Global Hydrology and Climate Center website at wwwghcc.msfc.nasa.gov located at the Marshall Space Flight Center in Huntsville, Alabama.)*

ENHANCED   UNENHANCED

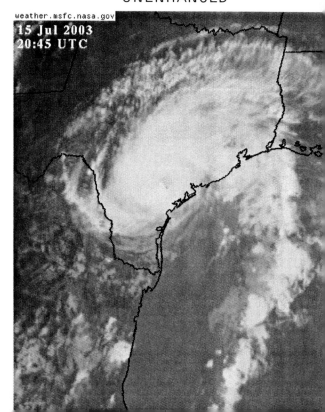

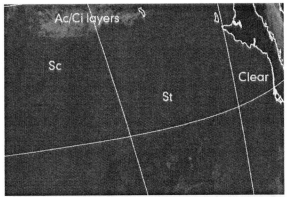

Infrared Imagery Cloud Types
Compare with equivalent imagery in Visible Imagery section

<u>Stratus</u> and fog are almost impossible to see on infrared imagery. As the cloud is rarely above 2,000 ft AGL, it is often so close to the ground that its thermal signature equals that of the surface. Only loops and the "appearance" or "disappearance" of warm or cool lakes attests to its presence on infrared imagery. In the example, the stratus layer off the Baja California coast is virtually invisible! Even the stratocumulus is tough to see. *(NOAA-14 1-km polar orbiter image; 19 July 2003 1522 UTC)*

<u>Cumulus</u> is often nearly invisible on infrared satellite imagery, particularly in tropical air masses where the convective condensation level is lower. However, high-based cumulus in relatively dry air masses will appear brighter and more well-defined, as seen here. *(NOAA-14 1-km polar orbiter image; 22 July 2003 2033 UTC)*

<u>Altocumulus</u> generally takes on a cooler, brighter look than cumulus and retains a smudgy, cellular or mottled character. If elements are convective, as with altocumulus castellanus, the pattern will look less sheetlike and more dotted. Shown here are grayish chaotic altocumulus layers over the Yukon Territories, which are the debris of daytime convection. Lingering cumulus appears as bright blobs. *(NOAA-14 1-km polar orbiter image; 24 July 2003 0000 UTC)*

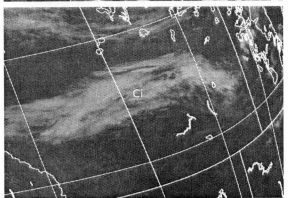

<u>Cirrus</u> has an unmistakable wispy texture. It may be mixed with lower clouds: all types in frontal systems and cumulonimbus in stormy patterns. Pure cirrus is typically light in texture such as this example over Alberta. It may appear colder and much brighter if it has substantial depth, such as with tropical moisture feeds. This is because it is thick enough to fully obscure infrared radiation from the ground. *(NOAA-14 1-km polar orbiter image; 19 July 2003 1522 UTC)*

Water Vapor Channel

Hang around any forecast office for long, and you'll get the idea that "water vapor imagery" and "moisture" go hand-in-hand. This is absolutely correct. The radiosonde observation network only detects small pieces of the moisture field across a given continent, and this makes water vapor imagery a powerful tool for filling in the blanks in a visual sense. The assumption is that moisture is associated with synoptic-scale ascent, while dry areas are associated with synoptic-scale subsidence.

Water vapor, particularly in the mid troposphere, tends to absorb radiation in the 6 to 7 micron band. Therefore the satellite imagery does not look directly for water vapor but rather suggests areas where radiation may have been absorbed by vapor in the atmosphere. The 6.7 micron band is picked up by special mercury cadmium telluride imagers on the weather satellite. As with infrared imagery, the scale is inverted so that strong radiation takes on a dark appearance while weak radiation looks bright.

Where a bright area is shown, it suggests the presence of moisture. This is actually a weak radiation signature, suggesting that enough moisture was present to absorb 6.7-micron radiation from the surface. A dark area indicates that all the radiation from the surface made it to the satellite without being attenuated.

With this in mind, there are some very important limitations with water vapor imagery:

■ It only works in the middle troposphere, mostly between 350 and 650 mb (12,000 and 25,000 ft). Therefore, whiteness (associated with moisture) can be present even though the low levels or upper levels are extremely dry.

■ It works best in warm atmosphere. Whiteness, the result of a lack of radiation, will also be produced in areas where it is so cold that no radiation can be emitted into space. This makes the imagery least useful in northern latitudes during the winter, where everything appears white in the 6.7-micron band.

■ It is degraded by the presence of clouds. Whiteness can be a layer of water droplets or ice (clouds) that are exceptionally thin, rather than a very deep, rich layer of water vapor.

Great sites with real-time data for this product . . .
○ NASA/GHCC — **wwwghcc.msfc.nasa.gov/GOES**
○ UCAR — **www.rap.ucar.edu/weather/satellite**
○ SSEC — **www.ssec.wisc.edu/data**
○ College of DuPage — **weather.cod.edu/analysis**
○ Universität Ulm — **meteosat.e-technik.uni-ulm.de**

■ GOES water vapor imagery is sensed at a wavelength of 6.7 microns and has a resolution of 8 km. Polar orbiter AVHRR systems do not produce water vapor imagery.

■ Clouds do not need to be present to show up on water vapor imagery. All that is needed is water vapor (a gas) in the middle troposphere to create a signature. Therefore moist bands can show up well before clouds begin forming on infrared or visible imagery.

■ A dark pixel indicates strong 6.7-micron radiation was received. This implies that the radiation was not absorbed by water vapor in the middle troposphere. Therefore we can assume that the middle troposphere is dry.

■ A bright pixel indicates weak 6.7-micron radiation was received. It implies one of several things: that radiation was absorbed by mid-tropospheric moisture (the general assumption) or that the surface temperature was too cold to generate radiation.

■ Very dark bands on water vapor imagery in the wake of a baroclinic storm system may be in proximity to a very strong jet max. This can help refine the jet max position. The location is usually on the periphery of the dark band (poleward) and the brighter area (equatorward).

■ Water vapor imagery is excellent for picking out the position of the subtropical jet (STJ). The STJ usually lies along the poleward periphery of a broad bulge of tropical moisture in the subtropical latitudes.

Right: Water vapor image. *(UCAR)*

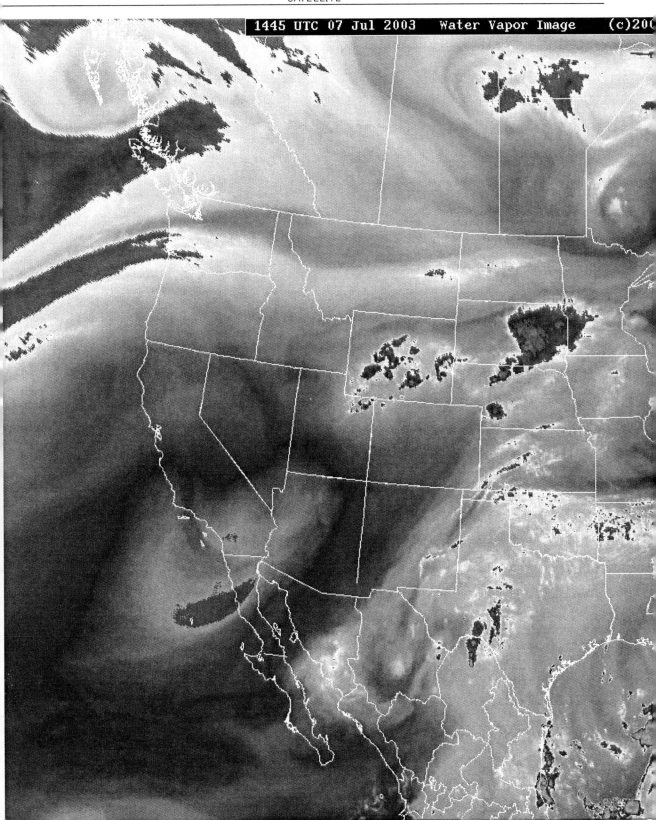

1445 UTC 07 Jul 2003   Water Vapor Image   (c)20

GOES Soundings

Since May 1994, when GOES-8 was put into operational service, an improved radiometer package and better satellite design have made satellite-based atmospheric soundings a reality. Such soundings entered operational use in July 1995. However, the technology and science is still in its infancy. The satellite sounding products are heavily dependent on output from numerical weather prediction models. The term "GOES sounding" is somewhat of a misnomer — a better description might be "NWP/ GOES sounding" to highlight that it is a fusion of the two technologies. However, this book will adhere to the standard naming conventions used in forecasting.

GOES Sounder sector scans are performed every 30 minutes, which scans the entire Earth's disk. Sensor data from 18 different infrared frequencies, ranging from 3.7 to 14.7 microns, plus the visible channel, are collected. This data has a resolution of about 8 km spaced every 10 km. This 8 km box produces an area on the Earth's surface known as a field of view (FOV), to distinguish this as a volumetric product rather than a point measurement. Each of the infrared channels are sensitive to radiation from a specific atmospheric layer. The word "layer" is an important distinction, because radiation is not sensed at individual levels but in layers. In many cases this sensitivity spans as much as 15,000 ft of depth, which has important implications for the sounding product.

For every 50 km a sounding is computed. The model sounding from the GFS run (formerly the AVN) is used as a first guess. In other words, it is assumed that the Eta sounding is what the GOES satellite is seeing. The satellite data and surface observation for the location are then automatically examined over an area as large as 50 km (ten fields of view along each axis) to see whether the column is free of clouds. Following this, radiation for the column is estimated and adjusted using surface data and GFS model variables. If the column is cloudy, a cloud top pressure is estimated, and the interrogation stops at this point. No satellite sounding can be computed.

For a clear column, the GFS sounding is adjusted so that its estimated radiation signature closely matches what the GOES satellite detects. The tweaked sounding is referred to as the "GOES sounding".

The suitability of GOES soundings to everyday forecasting problems is not yet clear. Much of the material dealing with GOES soundings has been in the arena of research or with very limited case studies, and a considerable amount of operational investigation still needs to be done. However, for those aware of the characteristics of the technology, it can be a valuable tool.

Great sites with real-time data for this product . . .
O NESDIS — **orbit-net.nesdis.noaa.gov/goes/soundings**
O U of W SSEC — **cimss.ssec.wisc.edu/goes/realtime**

■ The GOES sounding is actually an GFS forecast sounding with adjustments made using satellite-detected radiation signatures.

■ The term "GOES retrieval" is often used to describe the process of creating a GOES sounding.

■ NESDIS attempted to use the Eta model for a brief period, but reverted back to the GFS after discovering problems with the low-level moisture.

■ The model's temperature profile is changed little, sometimes not even perceptibly, by the GOES sounder. In many cases the profile is more representative of the GFS model than reality.

■ The model's moisture profile may be changed significantly by the GOES sounder. These changes are useful from a forecasting perspective.

■ Clouds, which radiate and absorb heat, contaminate the sample column and prevent GOES soundings from being made at a given location. Such locations are automatically skipped by sounding products.

■ GOES sounder data is most useful in regions that have no radiosonde coverage at all: within oceans and gulfs.

■ The GOES sounder data is used to produce estimated total precipitable water products.

Columbus, OH

KCMH
10 AUG 03
19GMT

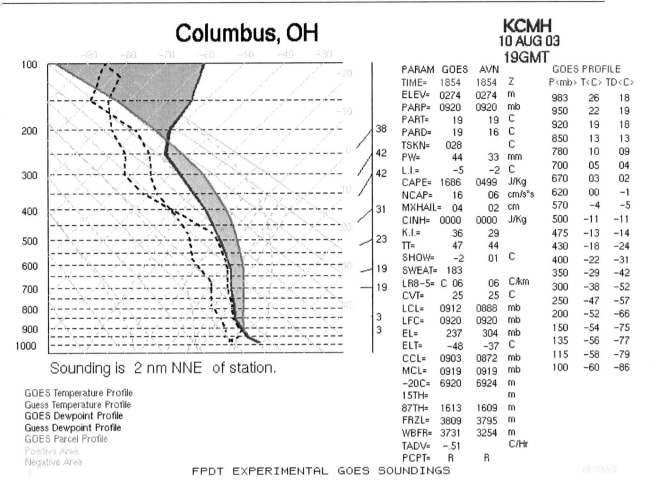

PARAM	GOES	AVN	
TIME=	1854	1854	Z
ELEV=	0274	0274	m
PARP=	0920	0920	mb
PART=	19	19	C
PARD=	19	16	C
TSKN=	028		C
PW=	44	33	mm
L.I.=	-5	-2	C
CAPE=	1686	0499	J/Kg
NCAP=	16	06	cm/s*s
MXHAIL=	04	02	cm
CINH=	0000	0000	J/Kg
K.I.=	36	29	
TT=	47	44	
SHOW=	-2	01	C
SWEAT=	183		
LR8-5= C	06	06	C/km
CVT=	25	25	C
LCL=	0912	0888	mb
LFC=	0920	0920	mb
EL=	237	304	mb
ELT=	-48	-37	C
CCL=	0903	0872	mb
MCL=	0919	0919	mb
-20C=	6920	6924	m
15TH=			m
87TH=	1613	1609	m
FRZL=	3809	3795	m
WBFR=	3731	3254	m
TADV=	-.51		C/Hr
PCPT=	R	R	

GOES PROFILE		
P<mb>	T<C>	TD<C>
983	26	18
950	22	19
920	19	18
850	13	13
780	10	09
700	05	04
670	03	02
620	00	-1
570	-4	-5
500	-11	-11
475	-13	-14
430	-18	-24
400	-22	-31
350	-29	-42
300	-38	-52
250	-47	-57
200	-52	-66
150	-54	-75
135	-56	-77
115	-58	-79
100	-60	-86

Sounding is 2 nm NNE of station.

GOES Temperature Profile
Guess Temperature Profile
GOES Dewpoint Profile
Guess Dewpoint Profile
GOES Parcel Profile
Positive Area
Negative Area

FPDT EXPERIMENTAL GOES SOUNDINGS

Above: Sample GOES sounding from <orbit-net.nesdis.noaa.gov/goes/soundings>, which offers one of the most detailed and timely selections available on the Internet. *(NOAA/NESDIS)*

Right: Graph showing the source of energy for four channels with respect to pressure (height). It can be seen that the energy occurs in very broad layers rather than at "points". *(From "Automated GOES Sounder Products", by Schmit, Wade, and Aune)*

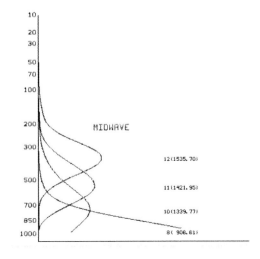

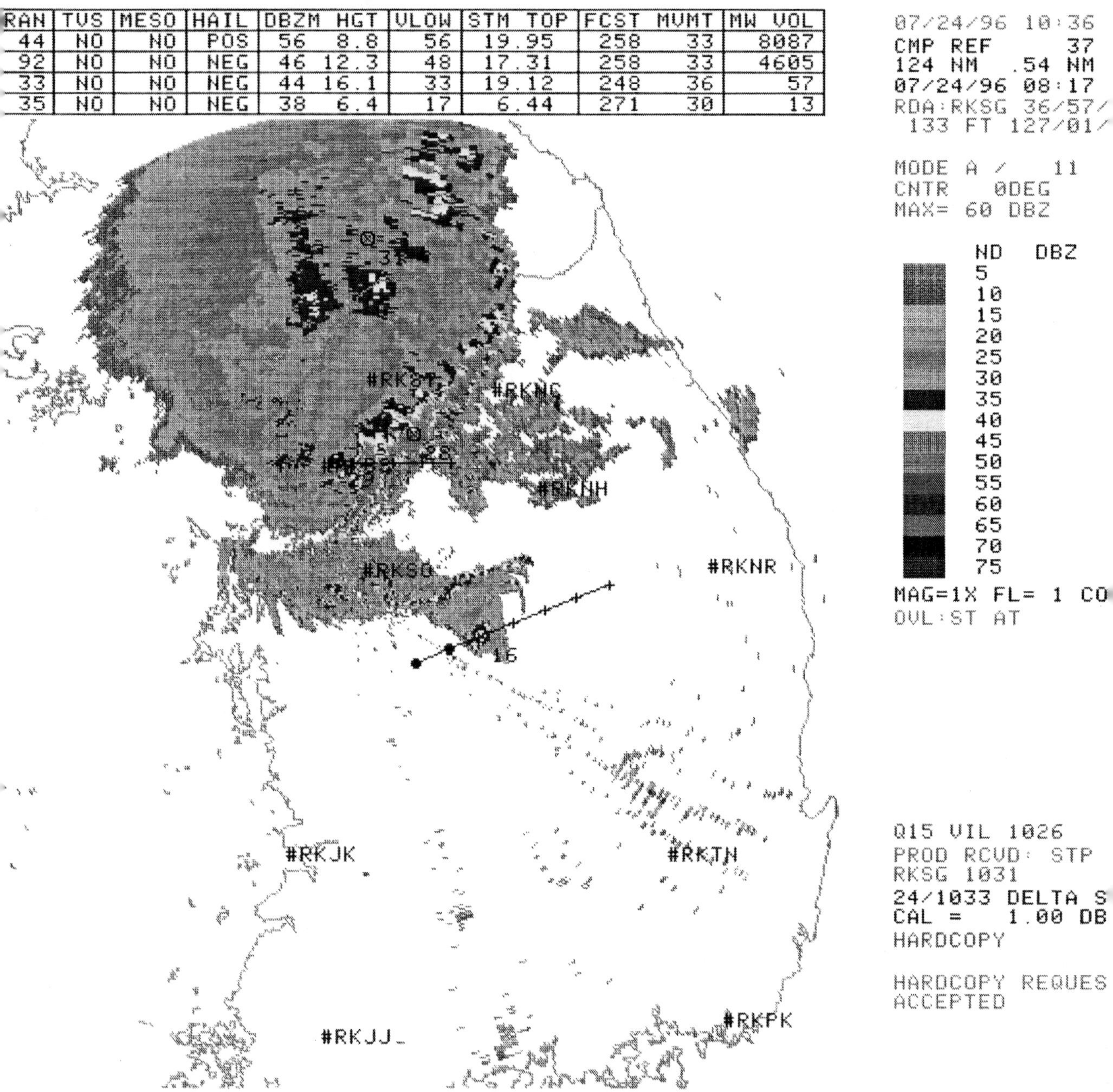

RAN	TVS	MESO	HAIL	DBZM	HGT	VLOW	STM TOP	FCST	MVMT	MW VOL
44	NO	NO	POS	56	8.8	56	19.95	258	33	8087
92	NO	NO	NEG	46	12.3	48	17.31	258	33	4605
33	NO	NO	NEG	44	16.1	33	19.12	248	36	57
35	NO	NO	NEG	38	6.4	17	6.44	271	30	13

07/24/96 10:36
CMP REF   37
124 NM .54 NM
07/24/96 08:17
RDA:RKSG 36/57/
133 FT 127/01/

MODE A /   11
CNTR   0DEG
MAX= 60 DBZ

ND DBZ
5
10
15
20
25
30
35
40
45
50
55
60
65
70
75

MAG=1X FL= 1 CO
OVL:ST AT

#RKST   #RKNC

#RKSS   25

#RKNH

#RKSG   #RKNR

16

Q15 VIL 1026
PROD RCVD: STP
RKSG 1031
24/1033 DELTA S
CAL =   1.00 DB
HARDCOPY

HARDCOPY REQUES
ACCEPTED

#RKJK   #RKTN

#RKPK

#RKJJ

RADAR

Above: We see two rarities: a coarse printout from the archaic first-generation NEXRAD PUP workstations, and a NEXRAD image from South Korea. The Department of Defense operates several WSR-88D sites outside of North America.

Radar

The entire radar section of this book is dedicated to the WSR-88D radar unit. Though this does not help most international readers, it is a badly needed supplement for American hobbyists and professionals. The WSR-88D radar has become the backbone of the United States weather radar network, and its data is extremely unique, saturated with presence on the Web, and in many instances its exact workings are not very well documented.

History

The roots of the NEXRAD (Next Generation Radar) Program go back to 1977-79. At this time, a network of WSR-74C and WSR-57 radars had been in operation for up to 20 years. Research was beginning to prove the value of velocity (Doppler) data in storm detection, and studies began to see if the radars could be upgraded. The Joint Doppler Operations Project was established in 1979 at the National Severe Storms Laboratory by the National Weather Service (NWS), the Federal Aviation Administration, and the U.S. Air Force. The task would be to oversee the development of a next-generation radar.

During much of the 1980s, engineering was performed by Paramax, a division of Unisys, with algorithm development largely completed by the National Severe Storms Laboratory. Radar units were delivered between 1990 to 1998, gradually converting the entire national radar network. In 1996 the last of the old-guard WSR-57 radars was retired in Charleston, South Carolina, marking the end of an era.

Engineering design

The WSR-88D is broken up into two main parts: the RDA and the RPG. The RDA (Radar Data Acquisition) unit consists of the antenna, transmitter, receiver, and signal processor. This produces a raw data stream consisting of reflectivity, velocity, and spectrum width data.

The RPG (Radar Products Generator) converts the raw data stream into an array of useful products, which are disseminated to all users.

Both the RDA and the RPG are controlled by a UCP (Unit Control Position) terminal, which is usually located remotely at the closest National Weather Service office. Up until the late 1990s, National Weather Service forecasters looked at the radar data using a proprietary PUP (Principal User Processor) workstation, however this has been largely replaced by WDSS (Warning Decision Support System) workstations running under Unix.

The power output of the WSR-88D radar is 750,000 watts. This is comparable to the transmitter of a large television station. Its klystron tube delivers a frequency of 2700 to 3000 MHz (10 to 11.1 cm; in the S-band) using a 28-foot dish that produces a beam 0.95° in width. A pulse length of 1.57 microseconds (1545 ft) is possible with the radar system. The radar collects reflectivity data at 250 m (820 ft) resolution, but this is downsized to 1 km before running detection algorithms and producing products.

The WSR-88D radome is 39 feet in diameter and made of rigid fiberglass. It is meant to protect the antenna from wind, lightning, and damaging weather. Since it only

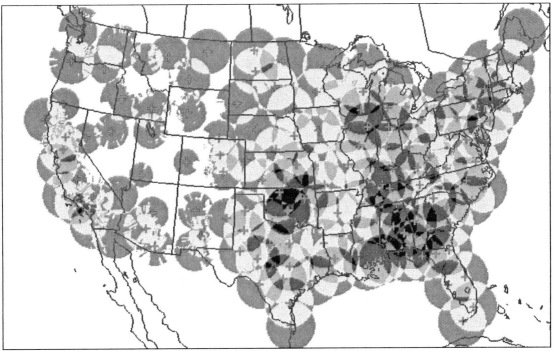

Above: Effective 128 nm radar coverage of the United States at 5 km (16400 ft) MSL, compensated for terrain and obstructions. Coverage is sparse in the Rockies. *("WSR-88D Radar Coverages", Jian Zhang, National Severe Storms Laboratory, 2001)*

causes a 0.6 dB signal loss it is almost transparent to the radar unit. The radar may sit upon a tower anywhere from 20 to 98 ft in height, depending on the terrain and obstructions.

Meteorological design

The WSR-88D is designed to operate in two radically different modes: *clear air* and *precipitation*. It can only operate in one of these modes at any given time. The main difference between the two is that clear air mode offers the advantage of greater sensitivity due to a slower antenna rotation rate, which allows more energy to be returned back to the radar. This comes at the cost of poor temporal resolution, with products generated half as often.

Another feature which can't be overlooked is the ability to provide velocity (Doppler shift) measurements of weather targets. This is accomplished by measuring the frequency shift of each bit of backscattered radiation. The velocity data allows measurement of any scatterer at any level.

WSR-88D Scan Strategy

The WSR-88D operates in one of four Volume Coverage Pattern (VCP) modes. Which one is in use is set manually by a human operator and has a profound influence on the radar products.

CLEAR AIR MODE (Mode B)

In each of the two clear air modes, the radar uses five identical elevation angles and completes a volume scan every ten minutes. This corresponds to a full sweep every two minutes. This slow sweep allows the radar to detect as many scatterers as possible.

■ VCP 31. The radar operates with a long pulse (better sensitivity) but with a lower pulse repetition frequency. This makes it more prone to velocity aliasing but less prone to range folding.

■ VCP 32. The radar operates with a short pulse (weaker sensitivity) but with a higher pulse repetition frequency. This makes it less prone to velocity aliasing but more prone to range folding.

PRECIPITATION MODE (Mode A)

■ VCP 11. The radar covers 14 elevation angles and completes a volume scan every five minutes. It uses short pulses (weaker sensitivity). The antenna completes a full sweep every 21 seconds. VCP 11 was designed for severe weather.

■ VCP 21. The radar covers 9 elevation angles. It completes a volume scan every six minutes. VCP 21 uses all low-level elevations of VCP 11 but omits many above 4.3°. Since it misses many of the upper elevations, it is not used when storms are close to the radar site. However by omitting the upper slices the radar has time to use a slower antenna rotation rate, completing a full sweep every 40 seconds. This allows better sensitivity to weak echoes. VCP 21 was designed for stratiform precipitation.

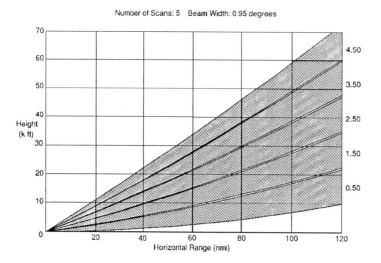

Illustrations. Nomograms showing the elevation of WSR-88D radar beams in degrees for each Volume Coverage Pattern (VCP). The graph allows you to see the height above the Earth's surface as a function of distance for each beam elevation.

Clear Air Scan
Volume Coverage Patterns 31 and 32

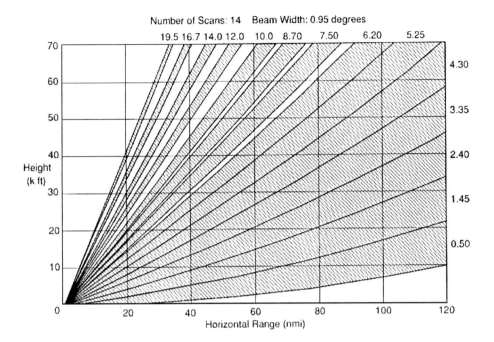

Number of Scans: 14   Beam Width: 0.95 degrees

Precipitation/Severe Weather Scan
Volume Coverage Pattern 11

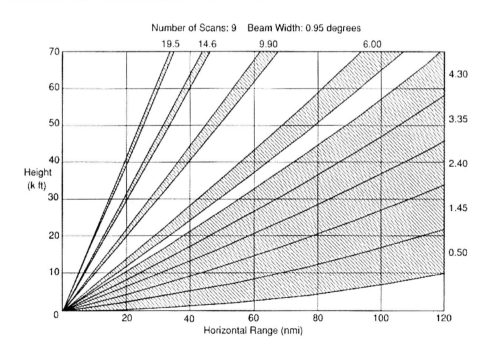

Number of Scans: 9   Beam Width: 0.95 degrees

Alternative Scan
Volume Coverage Pattern 21

Base Reflectivity

Radar energy is reflected from water droplets and ice particles back to the radar receiver. The stronger the reflection, the more "intense" the echo. Radar detects only precipitation. It does not detect clouds (water vapor). Base reflectivity can be contaminated by ground clutter and anomalous propagation. Insects and birds can produce large patterns of faint reflectivity around the radar site. Also the beam widens out to 2 miles in size 100 nm from the radar site, so small-scale storm features are lost at long ranges.

The WSR-88D NEXRAD radar products provide 0.54 nm (1 km) resolution out to 124 nm, and 1.1 nm (2 km) resolution out to 248 nm. Intensity is described in decibels of power reflected, or dBZ. The scale is logarithmic, so an increase of 3 dBZ is a doubling of power returned.

The technique of analyzing strong thunderstorms is a science in itself. Strong winds can shape the precipitation core into unique patterns, such as the hook echo, which is indicative of a tornado. A strong thunderstorm core which shifts more toward the edge of the cell, rather than remaining centered, is indicative of a severe thunderstorm. The biggest threat of severe weather is at the strong reflectivity gradient.

A feature called a "bright band" is often observed in stratiform winter precipitation situations. This is a ring that appears on the base reflectivity product, centered on the radar site. It occurs when the radar beam intersects a layer of snow melting into rain as it falls, which creates enhanced radar reflectivity. As the range and height to this feature is similar across the region, it appears at a constant range from the radar, and thus appears as a ring or a partial ring. The height of the feature can be easily estimated.

It must be remembered that the sweep of the radar beam is conical in shape; it is near the ground at the radar site and increases to higher heights at increasing distance from the radar site. Therefore echoes far from the radar are being sampled at a much higher elevation — as high as 15,000 ft at 100 miles from the radar. This makes it impossible to directly sample low-altitude features such as hook echoes at such ranges. Also a much larger volume is being sampled, so key storm features may be smeared out.

Great sites with real-time data for this product . . .
- CoD — **weather.cod.edu/analysis/radar.main.html**
- NWS — **www.nws.noaa.gov/radar**
- Canada MSC — **meteo.ec.gc.ca/radar**
- Weathertap ($) — **www.weathertap.com**
- Global — **www.weathermatrix.net/radar/data/world**

■ Most "local radar" views seen on television are base reflectivity. However anything covering an entire state or region will tend to be a composite reflectivity image (see following page). It is important to know the difference when making assumptions about weather systems. Quite often a composite reflectivity view can make a storm system appear worse than it really is!

■ In clear air mode, reflectivity shows echoes spanning -28 to 28 dBZ. In precipitation mode, echoes range from 5 to 70 dBZ. Websites typically assign radically different color sets to each mode so that it is immediately obvious which color set and radar mode is in effect. For example, precipitation mode is most often made up of greens and yellows, while clear air mode shows red and gray echoes.

■ NEXRAD grew out of a multiagency study from 1977 to 1979 at NSSL, followed by Federal funding in 1981. Full-scale radar production began in 1990. The first unit was delivered to Oklahoma City on May 24, 1990, and was also the first to be officially commissioned in February 1994.

■ Always be alert for suspicious echoes, such as chaff, birds, and solar spikes. They are surprisingly common.

■ The Product Code of base reflectivity is 19/R.

■ Radar intensity relationships
10 dBZ - Very light rain / light snow
20 dBZ - Light rain / heavy snow
30 dBZ - Moderate rain
40 dBZ - Heavy rain / thunder
50 dBZ - Torrential rain and thunder
60 dBZ - Thunder with rain and hail

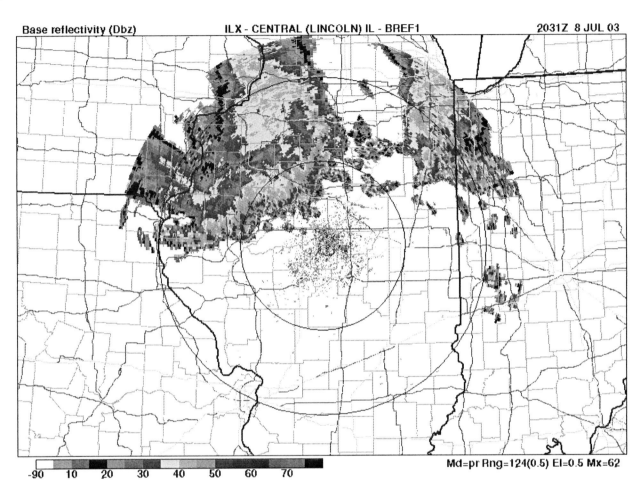

Base reflectivity (Dbz)   ILX - CENTRAL (LINCOLN) IL - BREF1   2031Z 8 JUL 03

-90   10   20   30   40   50   60   70   Md=pr Rng=124(0.5) El=0.5 Mx=62

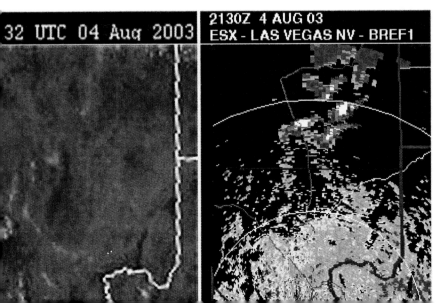

32 UTC 04 Aug 2003

2130Z 4 AUG 03
ESX - LAS VEGAS NV - BREF1

Above: Base reflectivity for a squall line event. Notice the echoes show more definition compared to the composite reflectivity image on the following page. The isolated cells ahead of the squall line are prime candidates for tornadoes and large hail. *(College of DuPage)*

Left: Echoes are not always weather. This is chaff released by Air Force pilots during a practice dogfight on the eastern edge of the Nevada Nellis Range. Compare with the satellite photo. Chaff may be indistinguishable from storms without the aid of supplementary tools.

Composite Reflectivity

The theory behind composite reflectivity is exactly the same as base reflectivity (see previous pages) However composite reflectivity examines not just one scan elevation but all of them. From this it displays the maximum reflectivity found in all of the "bins" vertically above a given location. In short, it displays the highest detected reflectivity value above that geographic location. This makes composite reflectivity suitable for displaying elevated layers, droplets suspended high in an updraft, and other features.

One of the best uses of composite reflectivity is in detecting the first signs of thunderstorm development. The first detectable echoes within a towering cumulus transitioning to a cumulonimbus cloud will typically occur at a height of 10,000 to 20,000 ft. This is usually *above* the lowest base reflectivity scan, except at distances beyond 100 miles from the radar. Therefore the first echoes will typically show up on one of the higher base reflectivity scans and appear on the composite reflectivity product.

Since composite reflectivity merges echo information at numerous levels, important structures seen on one base reflectivity frame can be completely lost. Hook echoes, vaults, bright bands, and other interesting features will invariably be smeared out or lost. Base reflectivity should always be monitored, especially during periods of severe weather.

Also it is not possible to draw conclusions about three-dimensional structure using composite reflectivity. Three-dimensional assumptions can be easily estimated using base reflectivity since the height is obvious to us as a function of scan height and range. For example, an intense signature close to the radar site on the 0.5° scan implies it is close to the ground. However this assumption cannot be made using composite reflectivity. Investigation of other products is necessary.

The composite reflectivity product is limited by the scan height. The radar antenna only rises to about 20 degrees, so it is incapable of seeing any tall echo near or above the radar site.

There is also a cost in terms of time. Base reflectivity products are available immediately after one full sweep of the radar beam. However, since composite reflectivity is a volumetric product, it will not be available until the entire volume scan is complete. While you are looking at a composite reflectivity product for eight minutes ago, a fresh base reflectivity scan may already be available for your use!

Great sites with real-time data for this product . . .
○ CoD — **weather.cod.edu/analysis/radar.main.html**
○ NWS — **www.nws.noaa.gov/radar**
○ Weathertap ($) — **www.weathertap.com**

■ Composite reflectivity is a depiction showing the highest reflectivity detected above a given location.

■ Precipitation areas look bigger than they really are at the surface. This is especially true of large thunderstorms and in dry air masses.

■ Many Internet sites choose to display composite reflectivity at 2.2 nm resolution with a range of 248 nm. Why this is often chosen is not clear, as it provides a very coarse product that is of marginal use for forecasting. However in coastal areas it can provide a long-range view of approaching storm systems. For less exotic use, on Weathertap you can opt for "Alternate Composite Reflectivity", which displays a standard 0.54 nm resolution product at 124 nm range. Such a product is used for our example.

■ The limitations of composite reflectivity include masking of features by echoes at other levels, inability to determine structure, scan height limitations, and time considerations since this is one of the last products generated in a volume scan.

■ The product code for Composite Reflectivity is 38/CR (for 2.2 nm 248 nm).

Above: Composite reflectivity for a squall line event. Compare to the base reflectivity image on the previous page. Note the "halo" of reflectivity surrounding the squall line itself. This is a reflection of super-cooled droplets and ice crystals within the anvil cloud. *(Weathertap)*

Below: Corresponding infrared satellite image. *(UCAR)*

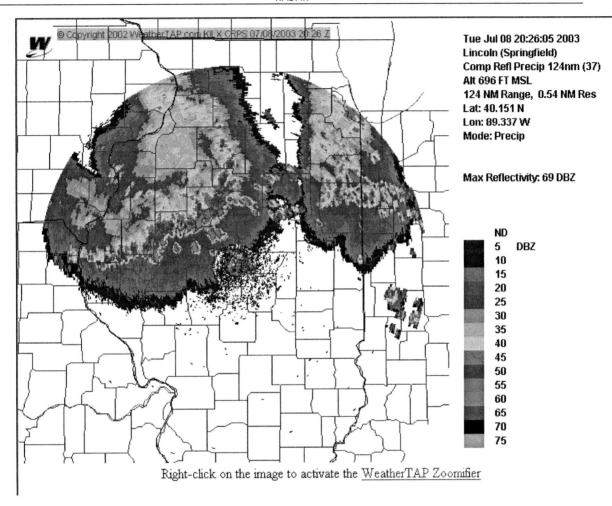

Tue Jul 08 20:26:05 2003
Lincoln (Springfield)
Comp Refl Precip 124nm (37)
Alt 696 FT MSL
124 NM Range, 0.54 NM Res
Lat: 40.151 N
Lon: 89.337 W
Mode: Precip

Max Reflectivity: 69 DBZ

ND
5   DBZ
10
15
20
25
30
35
40
45
50
55
60
65
70
75

Right-click on the image to activate the WeatherTAP Zoomifier

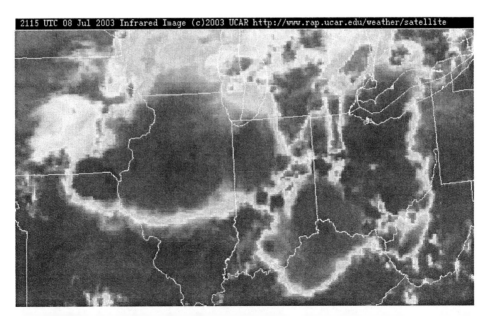

Velocity

In its simplest terms, the Radial Velocity product describes the radial velocity (along the beam) of scatterers within a given bin. The radar determines this by measuring the Doppler shift of the reflected energy. Since velocity is only available radially, this makes the product challenging to interpret. Tangential and pure two-dimensional motion cannot be measured; only assumed. However some key concepts can help the beginner.

The overall shape of the broad-scale negative and positive shading tends to outline the tropospheric wind flow. The radar swath defines a cone within the troposphere, so all heights are included in the scan. For example a spiral appearance to the broad-scale coloring suggests change in wind direction with height. A lack of a spiral appearance suggests unidirectional winds throughout the troposphere.

Small-scale circulations are analyzed by finding a couplet; in other words, a pair containing positive and negative velocity. The exact orientation of this couplet relative to the radar determines whether convergence, divergence, cyclonic rotation, or anticyclonic rotation is present (see illustration). When peak velocities of a couplet touch each other, velocity is expressed in terms of "gate-to-gate shear"; this usually only occurs with the tight rotation or convergent rotation signature of a tornado.

When possible, the Storm Relative Motion (SRM) product should be used to analyze a storm. This attempts to balance velocity data by compensating for the drift of features with the prevailing flow, and can help features stand out much better. For example, a couplet with -15 kt and +15 kt peaks will be masked if it is drifting away from the radar at 45 mph. In such a case the couplet will show velocities of +30 and +60 mph on Radial Velocity and will be difficult to see. The SRM product would subtract the 45 mph motion. The motion is automatically derived from an average of all storm velocities as determined by the Storm Tracking Algorithm.

Range folding is an artifact that occurs when the distance to a storm exceeds the maximum unambiguous range. Beyond this range the echo arrives after the next pulse has been transmitted and a false echo occurs. When the WSR-88D senses that this has occurred, the velocity data is usually shaded gray or purple to show that it has been corrupted.

Aliasing is another problem. The velocity of a scatterer may exceed the maximum unambiguous velocity (the Nyquist co-interval), which is the highest velocity observable by the radar given its current pulse settings. The radar contains a dealiasing algorithm that attempts to minimize this problem.

Great sites with real-time data for this product . . .
○ CoD — **weather.cod.edu/analysis/radar.main.html**
○ NWS — **www.nws.noaa.gov/radar**
○ Weathertap ($) — **www.weathertap.com**

■ Positive velocity is movement away from the radar. Negative velocity is movement toward the radar. These are key concepts that should be memorized.

■ The Storm Relative Motion product should not be used by itself to make assumptions about surface winds. The SRM product uses a storm-relative frame of motion, while the Radial Velocity product uses a ground-relative frame of motion. In a downburst situation, the SRM product can help locate mechanisms for high winds, while the radial velocity product suggests the actual winds experienced at the surface (relative to the radar, of course).

■ If you trace the border formed between the broad-scale negative and positive areas on the velocity scan, it can be used to judge the wind direction throughout the entire troposphere. At any given point along this line, the wind is perpendicular to the radar beam, blowing toward the positive velocity area. By tracing this line from the radar site to the outer range area, you can follow the wind direction from the ground to the upper troposphere or stratosphere. The wind speed is traced in a like manner by going outward from the radar site to the maximum range and finding the maximum wind velocity at each particular range.

■ Velocity products depend on a scatterer. If precipitation or other particles are not in an updraft, and thus showing no reflectivity, velocity signatures will not be detectable.

■ The Product Code for radial velocity is 27/V (25/V for 32 nm/0.13 nm)

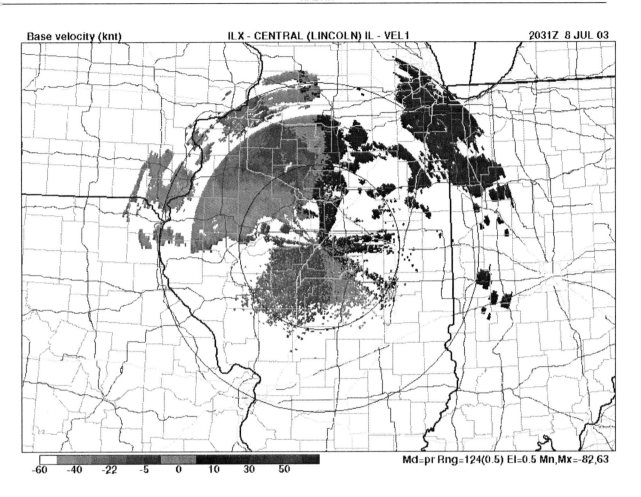

Base velocity (knt)   ILX - CENTRAL (LINCOLN) IL - VEL1   2031Z 8 JUL 03

-60   -40   -22   -5   0   10   30   50

Md=pr Rng=124(0.5) El=0.5 Mn,Mx=-82,63

Above: Velocity image for a summertime squall line event. Little can be determined from this black and white image. Access to color as well as the ability to zoom down to individual pixels are important. *(College of DuPage)*

Right: Fundamental structures for different types of small-scale velocity couplets. The orientation of the couplets relative to the radar determines what type of circulation is present.

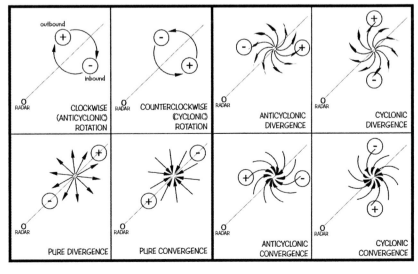

PURE MOTION
(Couplet either parallel or perpendicular to the radar beam)

COMBINED MOTION
(Couplet diagonal to the radar beam)

CLOCKWISE (ANTICYCLONIC) ROTATION

COUNTERCLOCKWISE (CYCLONIC) ROTATION

ANTICYCLONIC DIVERGENCE

CYCLONIC DIVERGENCE

PURE DIVERGENCE

PURE CONVERGENCE

ANTICYCLONIC CONVERGENCE

CYCLONIC CONVERGENCE

Spectrum Width

Spectrum width measures the variance in velocity within a given radar volume. Particles in any given volume are almost never moving cohesively at a single velocity. Turbulence, varying particle sizes, and different forces at work within the volume can all combine to cause varying trajectories and velocities. The velocity estimated by the radar in one specific bin is actually an average of all of these motions.

The variance in the motion corresponds to the spectrum width. This can be measured by examining the "width" of the Doppler shift that is returned to the radar. Low width will cause the reflected energy to peak at one very specific frequency, while high width will cause a broad dispersion of the echo at slightly different frequencies. A spectrum width is usually expressed as low (narrow) or high (broad).

One of the most significant studies of spectrum width relates to severe thunderstorms. A paper by Keith Browning and drawn upon by Leslie Lemon suggest that an updraft core normally contains air that ascends uniformly and smoothly, with turbulent flow largely dampened out. This suggests that the updraft may be found by locating a core of narrow spectrum width within the cloud.

There is some evidence that spectrum width products can help locate small tornadoes, gustnadoes, and waterspouts. Within a radar bin, a small tornado may not contain enough fast-moving scatterers to trigger a shear signature. However these scatterers would produce a wide range of velocities within that particular bin. The spectrum width product would return a high value. In a similar manner and at a much smaller scale of motion, spectrum width can help locate and measure areas of turbulence.

Another use of spectrum width is to identify suspected three-body scatter spike (TBSS) signatures, which are artifacts that seem to project behind a hail core along the beam radial. The presence of a high spectrum width can help suggest that the artifact is indeed a TBSS artifact.

In more quiescent weather patterns, spectrum width data can be used to help locate fronts and outflow boundaries. Often these features are easily identified, particularly in clear air mode, but at times they may be masked. Spectrum width can help confirm the validity of radial velocity data. A large spectrum width may indicate that the averaged radial velocity for that bin is not reliable. Finally, spectrum width may also help locate initial convective development.

Great sites with real-time data for this product . . .
O None are known to exist at this time.

- Spectrum width tends to increase with range from the radar. This is a natural consequence of beam broadening: as the beam widens, there is bound to be an increasingly large range of particle motions.

- Spectrum width values are not affected by VCP changes, though clear-air modes will provide greater accuracy.

- Spectrum width is one of the three base products of the WSR-88D, in addition to reflectivity (power) and velocity.

- The study of spectrum width as related to operational forecast problems is still a mysterious area in meteorology, and it can be very difficult to find references that provide guidance for its use.

- The idea of using spectrum width to identify small vortices was pioneered in 1995 by Joseph Golden and Carin Goodall-Gosnell, and in another 1995 paper by Waylon Collins. Both papers studied waterspout events in the southeastern United States and related them to WSR-88D spectrum width data.

- WSR-88D spectrum width data has been the focus of several studies by UCAR and other institutions designed to help reduce the risk of clear air turbulence to aircraft.

- Weak reflectivity bordering on the noise threshold for the radar will cause erratic spectrum estimates and noisy spectrum width returns.

- The product code is 30/SW (124/0.54 nm) and 28/SW (32/0.13 nm).

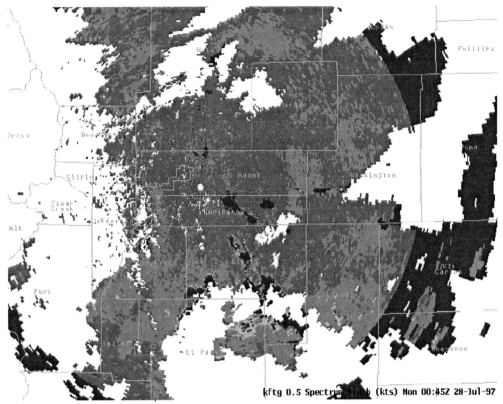

kftg 0.5 Spectrum Width (kts) Mon 00:45Z 28-Jul-97

Above: WSR-88D spectrum width product from the Denver WSR-88D. *(UCAR)*

Right: Spectrum width has had its best success in turbulence detection experiments. The NASA TCAD (Turbulence Characterization and Detection) program was a partnership between NASA, NCAR, Colorado State University, the South Dakota School of Mines and Technology, Rockwell-Collins, and Allied Signal. Here is shown the track of a test aircraft during the 1999 experiment, compared with the spectrum width detected by a ground-based radar. *(UCAR)*

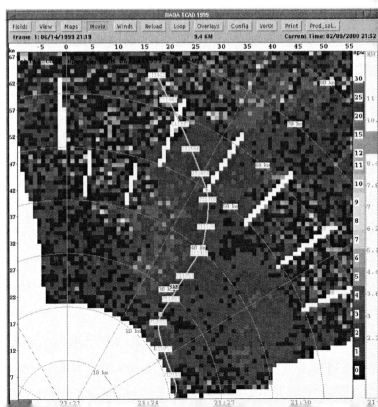

Precipitation Total

The Precipitation Total product actually refers to three specific products generated by the NEXRAD site. These are 1-hour precipitation, 3-hour precipitation, and storm total precipitation. These provide a graphic estimate of precipitation totals within 124 nm of the radar site. The data is expressed as 16 levels ranging from 0 to 15 inches.

The Precipitation Total product is excellent for monitoring areas that have had excessive precipitation. These areas may be subject to flooding. It can also reveal where grounds are saturated, which can further compound flooding and can feed moisture back into a convective situation through evaporation. The product can determine where heavy snow has fallen. Hydrologists will use Precipitation Totals to find where basins are approaching saturation and where streams might reach flood stage.

If no precipitation, as determined by the precipitation totals algorithm, has fallen within 124 nm of the site after more than an hour, the storm total precipitation (STP) product is automatically reset and all plots show a zero precipitation total. However, during long rain events the storm total period may exceed 24 hours.

As with many other products, precipitation total estimates are limited by the tilt of the radar antenna, which reaches no higher than 19.5°. Not all of a precipitation shaft which is very close to the antenna will be sampled. The problem usually occurs within 20 nm of the site for convective precipitation and within 10 nm of the site for stratiform precipitation.

The data is easily contaminated by ground clutter and anomalous propagation. Chaff (from military aircraft) will produce false totals and produce plots that look unusually like precipitation. When bright bands occur during cold weather events, these will artifically distort the totals.

Fast-moving systems will distort the precipitation total pattern, as the storm will move across multiple bins between scans. This will produce a herringbone pattern in the precipitation total "trails" left by storms.

Hail will cause overestimation of rainfall amounts, as hail particles reflect much more power back to the radar than water droplets do. The three-body scattering spike signatures can also "lay down" precipitation values behind the hail core, where no precipitation actually exists.

Great sites with real-time data for this product . . .
- ○ CoD — **weather.cod.edu/analysis/radar.main.html**
- ○ NWS — **www.nws.noaa.gov/radar**
- ○ Weathertap ($) — **www.weathertap.com**

■ The depiction of precipitation totals was changed from Cartesian 1.1 nm blocks to standard polar coordinate format effective with NEXRAD Build 9 in late 1996.

■ It is helpful to conduct a study of your local area and determine whether the radar tends to underestimate or overestimate precipitation. Be sure to use official day-to-day readings at an airport weather station for the best results, rather than using extreme rainfall amounts from unknown sources.

■ Storm total precipitation values are reset when no precpitation totals are detected by the algorithm for at least one full hour.

■ Storm total precipitation is not confined to a specific time limit and may exceed 24 hours.

■ There is no quality control of the precipitation product at any stage. It is to be used at your own risk.

■ Plots near military operating areas are frequently degraded by chaff released by military aircraft during mock dogfights. This includes the area north of Las Vegas, the area west and southwest of Phoenix, and the region southwest of Salt Lake City.

■ Precipitation total estimates are corrupted by precipitation too close to the radar antenna, by ground clutter or chaff, by fast moving storms, and by hail cores.

■ The Product Codes for precipitation products are 78/OHP (1-hr); 79/THP (3-hr); and 80/STP (storm total).

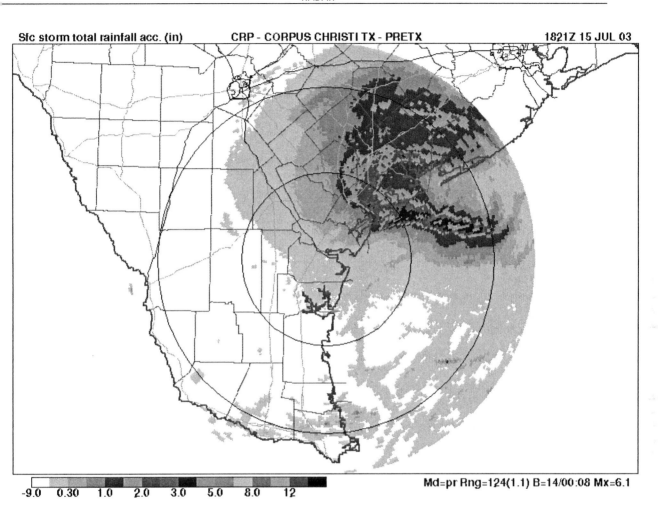

Sfc storm total rainfall acc. (in)   CRP - CORPUS CHRISTI TX - PRETX   1821Z 15 JUL 03

-9.0   0.30   1.0   2.0   3.0   5.0   8.0   12

Md=pr Rng=124(1.1) B=14/00:08 Mx=6.1

Above: Storm total precipitation product generated during the landfall of Hurricane Claudette on July 15, 2003. *(College of DuPage)*

Right: A National Weather Service hydrologist adjusts a 1-hour precipitation total estimate from the Fort Worth WSR-88D before feeding it into a local model. This quality control procedure makes for better runoff and soil saturation estimates, improving the quality of flood forecasts. *(Tim Vasquez)*

Vertically Integrated Liquid

Vertically Integrated Liquid, or VIL, examines all of the 2.2 x 2.2 nm bins above a given location and adds them to estimate the total water content above a given location. The estimation of liquid precipitation within each bin uses complex equations that relate reflectivity to drop-size distribution and water content. VIL is initially calculated in terms of kilograms of water per square meter, then is integrated throughout the column to produce a volumetric measure in kilograms per cubic meter.

The most important strength of VIL is that, being an additive total of all echoes in the vertical, it allows an immediate assessment of which storms are most important. A cyclic increase and decrease in VIL values indicates a multicell thunderstorm structure, though this could also indicate a storm that is not being adequately sampled in the upper levels (especially in VCP 21). Persistent high VIL values are usually associated with supercells.

The VIL value is often a function of the storm's updraft strength, as only a strong updraft can loft and condense large quantities of water vapor.

Furthermore, VIL has formed one of the strongest links to observed hail size. In fact, during the early 1990's forecasters were urged to use VIL to assess the hail threat. The introduction of a new Hail Detection Algorithm, which properly links the melting level to significant storm tops and to the surface, has allowed for better indicator of hail.

VIL is affected by any process or phenomena that distorts reflectivity values. Therefore, chaff, bright bands, and three-body scatter spikes can all corrupt a VIL value.

A storm that is tilted will produce artificially low VIL values. A tilted storm spreads its footprint across multiple vertical bins, thinning out the VIL response.

A fast moving storm will move from one horizontal grid square to the next between each elevation scan. When the volume scan is complete, the storm may have crossed ten grid squares or more (i.e., a storm moving 40 mph will move 4 miles during a volume scan). This will distort the VIL calculations and produce a lower VIL value spread across a wider area.

Once the storm becomes 40 nm or further from the radar, gaps between the elevation scans become increasingly wider and more of the storm becomes unsampled. The bins also become very wide, and intense cores may not be fully detected. Therefore VIL values tend to be overestimated beyond about 110 nm.

- VIL is an indirect measure of the available precipitation at a given spot. It can be thought of as reflectivity summed with height.

- There is no magic number for VIL values. They vary according to the season and type of weather system. Trends and immediate differences in VIL values are more meaningful.

- VIL values are the least reliable in VCP 21 due to the wide elevation gaps present above 4.3°.

- VIL is adversely affected by storm tilt, fast storm motion, elevation gaps, proximity to the radar, and operation in VCP 21.

- VIL will not be adequately represented closer than about 20 nm to the radar, as the radar antenna is limited to a tilt of 19.5°.

- The equation for VIL is:

$$VIL = SUM \; 3.44 \times 10^{-6} \, [Z]^{4/7} \, dh$$

where Z is the average radar reflectivity within a layer and dh is the thickness of that layer. The result is VIL in kg/m^2.

- You may encounter the term "VIL density". This refers to VIL divided by the echo top (it is usually expressed in units of 1000). So a storm with a low top would have a high VIL density, given the same VIL value. The idea is that it is normal for shallow storms to have low VIL values and for deep storms to have high VIL values, and to help identify any departure from this basic relationship.

- The Product Code of VIL is 57/VIL.

Great sites with real-time data for this product . . .
○ CoD — **weather.cod.edu/analysis/radar.main.html**
○ NWS — **www.nws.noaa.gov/radar**
○ Weathertap ($) — **www.weathertap.com**

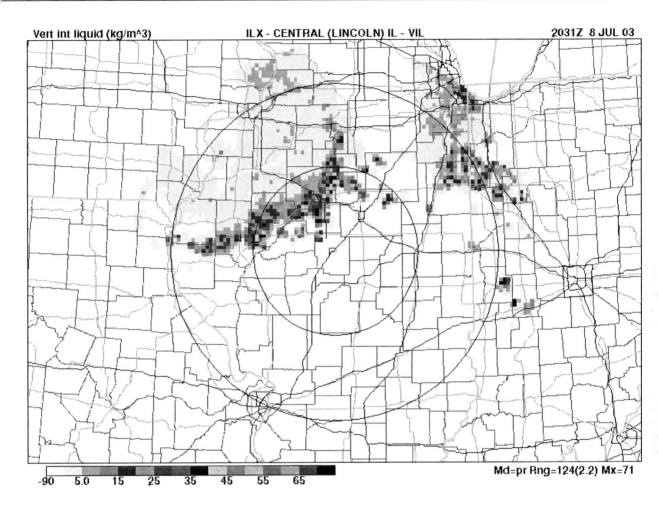

Vert int liquid (kg/m^3)   ILX - CENTRAL (LINCOLN) IL - VIL   2031Z 8 JUL 03

-90   5.0   15   25   35   45   55   65   Md=pr Rng=124(2.2) Mx=71

Above: VIL values in a squall line. Radar image from College of DuPage Nexlab. *(College of DuPage)*

Right: A cross-section of a storm shows the simplified concept of VIL. Arbitrary reflectivity values are shown within the storm cloud (outlined). The values are summed to produce a total. Notice how the lowest reflectivity scans miss any significant precipitation, but VIL detects the higher core. Composite reflectivity is similar in principle and would show the highest value in each vertical stack.

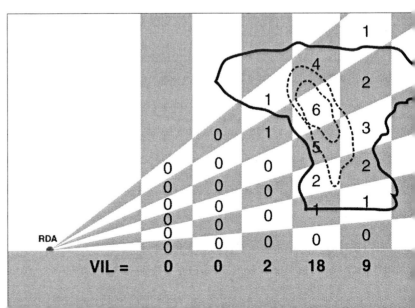

Echo Tops

The Echo Tops product is a processed type of image. The region is divided up into grid boxes measuring 2.2 nm square, and all scans are analyzed to find the highest grid box that exceeds 18.5 dBZ. The center beam height for the highest scan meeting the reflectivity threshold is the echo top.

The biggest problem with this product is that the echo tops are not always sampled, or may be sampled too coarsely.

The first type of problem is related to the antenna's maximum tilt, which is 19.5°. As a result, when storms exceed 30,000 ft within 15 nm of the radar or 50,000 ft within 25 nm of the radar, the radar is unable to scan clear air above the storm and the echo top is underestimated.

Elevation gaps are a significant problem, in which are slices "skipped" by the scan strategy. This is a significant problem in VCP 21 which has only four scans between 4.3° and 19.5°. For example, imagine a storm with a top of 55,000 ft located 55 nm from the radar. The 6° elevation intersects this range at 60,000 ft and the 4.3° elevation intersects at 37,000 ft. Unfortunately it is only the 4.3° elevation that detects the storm, so the elevation is counted as 37,000 ft. As an echo gets closer, its elevation seems to drop as it descends the beam until it is detected on the next highest elevation slice and jumps to another height. This behavior causes the "stairstep" pattern often seen on Echo Tops products. It is most prominent when stratiform tops are present.

Beam width is also a detrimental factor. At 120 nm the width of the radar beam spreads to about 13,000 ft. This means that a storm registering a top of 48,000 ft top may actually be topping out at anywhere between 38,500 and 51,500 ft.

All of this may be further compounded by the limited resolution of the Echo Tops product. Storms are rounded into blocks of 5,000 ft. As a result, a storm with a height of 29,000 ft will fall into the 25,000 ft to 30,000 ft block, and may be interpreted to be slightly weaker than it really is.

The threshold value of 18.5 dBZ means that an echo top with a reflectivity of less than 18.5 dBZ will be cut off. An echo top, which includes an overshoot or anvil top, may be actually higher than what is depicted.

Finally, the echo top product does not compensate for sidelobes, which are artificial spikes that are generated due to the extreme reflectivity near hail cores. This may lead to the product *overestimating* echo tops.

Great sites with real-time data for this product . . .
○ CoD — **weather.cod.edu/analysis/radar.main.html**
○ NWS — **www.nws.noaa.gov/radar**
○ Weathertap ($) — **www.weathertap.com**

■ The Echo Tops product does not determine the actual top of each storm but instead looks for the highest bin that exceeds 18.5 dBZ.

■ Echo top is not a direct indicator of storm severity. Tropopause height, which varies with season, and temperatures above the tropopause all have an influence on a storm's height.

■ A storm does not need to be present for an echo top to be detected. The product will estimate the tops of cirrus, stratiform rain, and thunderstorms, with each treated just the same.

■ Thunderstorm tops are likely to be higher than what the echo top product indicates, since the product cuts off detection below the 18.5 dBZ threshold value.

■ Thunderstorm tops may be lower than what the echo top product indicates when significant amounts of large hail are present within the storm. This will cause three-body scattering spikes, which are spurious false echoes that extend behind and above the storm.

■ An echo top that is increasing in height may indicate a strengthening storm, with the opposite true for a weakening storm. An echo top decreasing very rapidly may indicate a collapsing updraft, with the possibility of downburst damage or a tornado at the surface.

■ Echo tops are usually underestimated, but may be overestimated when severe hail is present within the storm.

■ The product code for the Echo Top product is 41/ET.

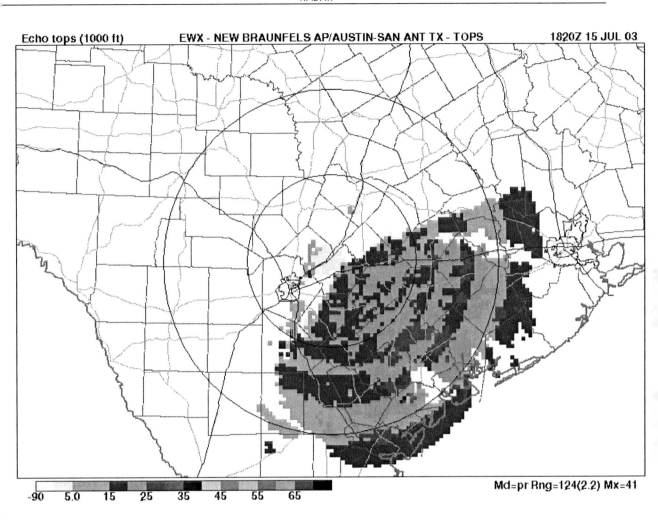

Echo tops (1000 ft)   EWX - NEW BRAUNFELS AP/AUSTIN-SAN ANT TX - TOPS   1820Z 15 JUL 03

-90   5.0   15   25   35   45   55   65   Md=pr Rng=124(2.2) Mx=41

Above: Echo tops product generated during the landfall of Hurricane Claudette on July 15, 2003. *(College of DuPage)*

Right: This diagram demonstrates the problems caused by elevation gaps as a storm draws closer. This type of problem is worst in VCP 21.

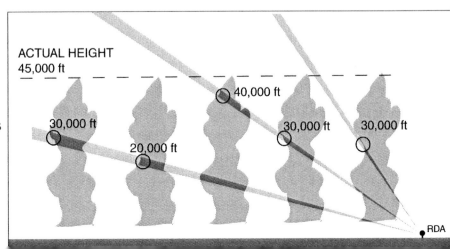

Storm Tracking Information (STI)

The purpose of the Storm Tracking Information product is to identify storm centroids and display their past, current, and projected locations. It uses the Storm Cell Identification and Tracking (SCIT) Algorithm, which replaced the old Storm Series Algorithm that was phased out with NEXRAD Build 9 in late 1996.

First the Storm Segments algorithm is run. One-dimensional storm segments are located by searching along a radial (i.e. at different azimuths at a constant distance) for one-dimensional runs of contiguous high reflectivities. If a series of high reflectivities has sufficent radial length to meet or exceed a parameter called the "overlap threshold", it is classified as a storm segment.

The Storm Centroids algorithm then runs. It gathers all storm segments and attempts to build two-dimensional representations of each storm. This produces a storm component. Each storm component is checked to see if it meets the minimum accepted size. Generally a size of 2.2 nm is considered sufficient. If it does not meets the size criteria, it is deleted. Each storm component is measured and assigned a "disk" that represents its location and radius.

When this is complete, storm components are resolved into three dimensions by looking at all elevations, measuring overlap of components, and determining an overall centroid for the storm.

At this point, the Storm Tracking Information algorithm executes. The algorithm's job is to relate each storm found in a current volume scan to a storm found in a previous volume scan. The algorithm starts with the largest storm centroid and works down to the smallest ones, linking current storm centroids to those from previous volume scans. This builds a track history. There are also sanity checks that are performed. A storm motion change over time must not exceed 90 degrees from the last scan. A storm centroid may also not have changed mass by more than one order of magnitude.

Finally the Storm Position Forecast algorithm is run. Each storm's anticipated motion during the upcoming hour is made by a simple extrapolation of its average direction and speed of movement. The algorithm also checks its work; if it has performed poorly, no forecasted positions are displayed. However if it has done a good job, forecast centroids for the next four volume scans are displayed. No projection is made for new storms.

Great sites with real-time data for this product . . .
○ Weathertap ($) — **www.weathertap.com**

■ The Storm Cell Identification and Tracking (SCIT) algorithm identifies thunderstorm cells and plots a history of paths and a projected track for each detected cell in the volume scan.

■ The SCIT algorithm was formerly known as the Storm Series Algorithm. This older algorithm focused exclusively on cells that were 30 dBZ or greater and lacked a sophisticated identification scheme.

■ The algorithm detects storms by looking for specific reflectivity patterns in increasingly higher dimensions, starting with storm segments (one dimension), storm centroids (two dimensions), and storm components (three dimensions).

■ Unusual structures, especially linear configurations seen in squall lines, will cause serious problems with the SCIT algorithm.

■ Forecast tracks are based only on previous movement. The algorithm does not forecast changes in intensity, path, or speed, and will not predict deviant movement.

■ A history track that shows a curve deviating from the mean tropospheric flow or from other cells may signal that the storm has transitioned to a severe phase.

■ Graphics display workstations such as WDSS often have a product available called "Cell Trends". This shows, for a given cell, its cell top, cell base, height of the storm centroid, its maximum reflectivity, probability of hail, probability of severe hail, cell-based VIL, and maximum reflectivity.

■ The product code is 58/STI.

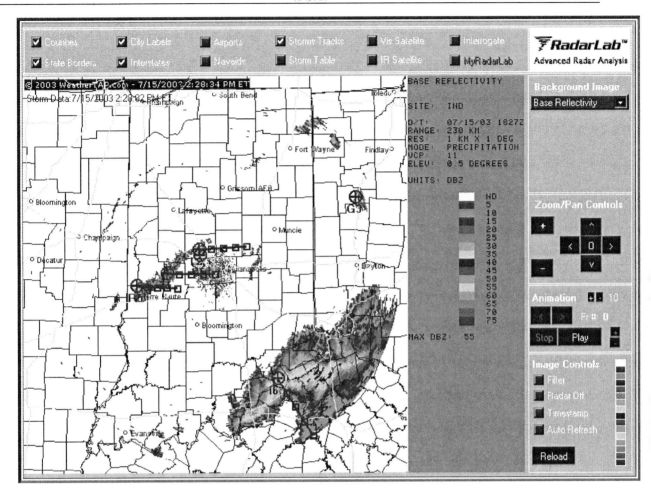

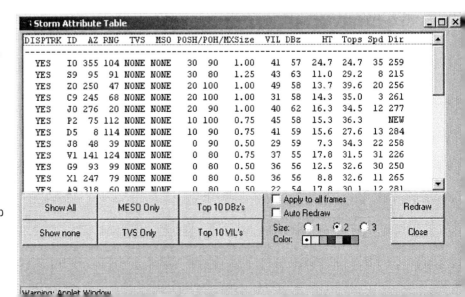

Above: Weathertap is among the few Internet radar providers that offers storm tracking information. It is part of their RadarLab option. However it appears only future plots are available (not history data) and at times the plots can be difficult to read. *(Weathertap)*

Right: Storm Attribute Table offered by Weathertap shows data for each cell.

DISPTRK	ID	AZ	RNG	TVS	MSO	POSH/POH/MXSize			VIL	DBz	HT	Tops	Spd	Dir
YES	IO	355	104	NONE	NONE	30	90	1.00	41	57	24.7	24.7	35	259
YES	S9	95	91	NONE	NONE	30	80	1.25	43	63	11.0	29.2	8	215
YES	Z0	250	47	NONE	NONE	20	100	1.00	49	58	13.7	39.6	20	256
YES	C9	245	68	NONE	NONE	20	100	1.00	31	58	14.3	35.0	3	261
YES	J0	276	20	NONE	NONE	20	90	1.00	40	62	16.3	34.5	12	277
YES	P2	75	112	NONE	NONE	10	100	0.75	45	58	15.3	36.3		NEW
YES	D5	8	114	NONE	NONE	10	90	0.75	41	59	15.6	27.6	13	284
YES	J8	48	39	NONE	NONE	0	90	0.50	29	59	7.3	34.3	22	258
YES	V1	141	124	NONE	NONE	0	80	0.75	37	55	17.8	31.5	31	226
YES	G9	93	99	NONE	NONE	0	80	0.50	36	56	12.5	32.6	30	250
YES	X1	247	79	NONE	NONE	0	80	0.50	36	56	8.8	32.6	11	265
YES	A9	318	60	NONE	NONE	0	80	0.50	22	54	17.8	30.1	12	281

Hail Index Overlay

The Hail Index is designed to display whether a storm's structure is conducive to hail formation. It incorporates the new Hail Detection Algorithm (HDA), which replaces the old Hail Index Algorithm that was phased out with NEXRAD Build 9 in late 1996. The new algorithm provides more robust detection capability, along with a new set of statistics for the end user such as hail size. An upgrade in 1998 allowed the generation of hail probability. Its input is storm centroids and components from the Storm Cell Identification and Tracking (SCIT) algorithm, along with user-defined melting level information.

The HDA produces three quantities for each location where hail is flagged: *Probability Of Hail* (POH), *Probability Of Severe Hail* (POSH), and *Maximum Expected Hail Size* (MEHS). In all instances, the difference in elevation between the melting level and the radar are factored in, so results are valid for the radar's elevation. Locations at different elevations, especially in higher terrain, must be evaluated accordingly.

The Probability Of Hail parameter determines the chance of any hail of any size reaching the Earth's surface. It looks for the height of the 45 dBZ echo above the melting level. According to this algorithm, if the 45 dBZ echo is 2 km above the melting level the POH is about 20%, and if it exceeds 6 km the POH rises to 100%.

The Probability Of Severe Hail runs a process called the Severe Hail Index (SHI). This process uses storm components from the SCIT algorithm as input "objects" and relates reflectivities to melting level data. It outputs a SHI value in joules per meter per second. From this, a POSH probability value is determined.

The Maximum Expected Hail Size uses only the SHI data, and uses a simple function that increases the expected hail size as the severe hail index grows. It is considered to be the most difficult part of the forecasts output by the HDA, since it cannot forecast unusual hail shapes and minor elevation differences.

How does the algorithm perform? So far it has received excellent reviews. A study done at NWS Wichita revealed that the HDA tends to overestimate hail size, but works very well in storms that develop in strong mid-level flow.

It must also be pointed out that the hail algorithm may fail in unusual structures, which include highly sheared storms and deviant movers. It may also fail in squall lines, since the Storm Tracking algorithms have trouble with linear structures. Furthermore the algorithm needs to be able to measure the depth of a storm for best results, therefore it doesn't work well when it is too close to the radar site.

> Great sites with real-time data for this product . . .
> ○ None are known to exist at this time.

■ By convention, the symbol for hail is a triangle that points upward. Probable hail is identified by a hollow triangle. Positive hail is identified by a filled triangle.

■ The original NEXRAD hail detection algorithm (HDA) was based on Leslie Lemon's 1978 storm structure concept and defined by Pio Petrocchi, John Smart, and Ron Alberty in 1982-85.

■ The old HDA was based on seven weighted questions, in order of increasing importance: does the highest storm component reach 8 km or more; does the storm's maximum reflectivity exceed 55 dBZ; is the low-level storm component north of one at a higher level; does the storm exhibit tilt; is the mid-level reflectivity (5 to 12 km) greater than 50 dBZ; does overhang of more than 4 km exist; and does the highest storm component exist above an overhang. The resulting score was flagged as either probable or positive.

■ The new Hail Detection Algorithm was developed in the mid-1990s primarily by Arthur Witt, with important contributions from J. T. Johnson, Pam MacKeen, DeWayne Mitchell, Greg Stumpf, Mike Eilts, and Kevin Thomas of the National Severe Storms Laboratory.

■ The MEHS is calculated by the HDA as:

$$MEHS = 2.54 \times SHI^{0.5}$$

where MEHS is in millimeters and SHI is the severe hail index in joules per meter per second.

■ The product code is 59/HI.

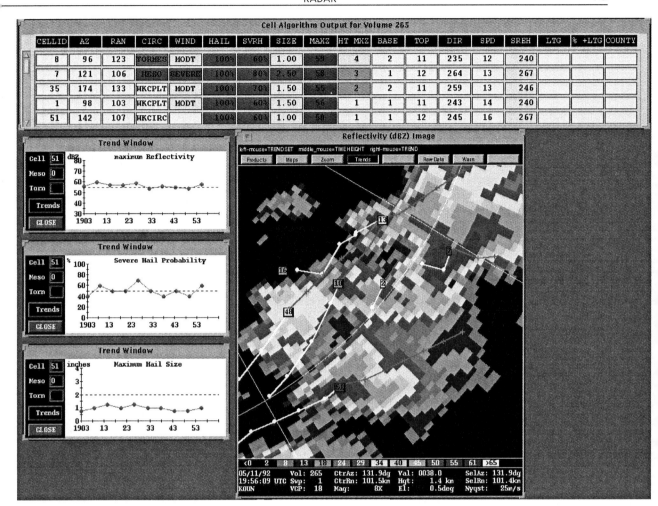

Cell Algorithm Output for Volume 265

CELLID	AZ	RAN	CIRC	WIND	HAIL	SVRH	SIZE	MAXZ	HT MXZ	BASE	TOP	DIR	SPD	SREH	LTG	% +LTG	COUNTY
8	96	123	TORMES	MODT	100%	60%	1.00	59	4	2	11	235	12	240			
7	121	106	MESO	SEVERE	100%	80%	2.50	58	3	1	12	264	13	267			
35	174	133	WKCPLT	MODT	100%	70%	1.50	55	2	2	11	259	13	246			
1	98	103	WKCPLT	MODT	100%	60%	1.50	56	1	1	11	243	14	240			
51	142	107	WKCIRC		100%	60%	1.00	50	1	1	12	245	16	267			

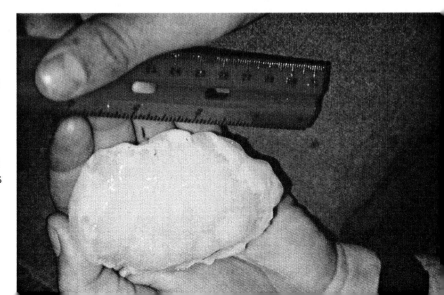

Above: NSSL demonstrator display of the Hail Detection Algorithm. *(NSSL)*

Right: Hailstone collected during Project Vortex. The oblate shape of the hailstone reveals some of the problems with trying to determine an exact forecast of hail size. *(NSSL photo)*

Mesocyclone Detection Algorithm

The NEXRAD Mesocyclone Detection Algorithm (MDA) pairs up base velocity information with processing power to determine the location of thunderstorm mesocyclones. The idea is not to take the responsibility away from the forecaster, but to provide the means to identify a potentially dangerous storm that might otherwise go unnoticed. The algorithm also identifies areas of uncorrelated shear which alerts the forecaster to rotation in a suspect area that is below the physical thresholds for a mesocyclone.

A mesocyclone is a region of strong, consistent rotation within a thunderstorm. It typically measures several miles in diameter and may carry tangential winds of over 40 mph. A mesocyclone signifies a very strong, organized updraft, and is often a precursor to tornado development. The vast majority of tornadoes are spawned within a mesocyclone, and perhaps all supercells contain a mesocyclone. Mesocyclones are typically cyclonic but a few may be anticyclonic. They usually develop at mid-levels and descend to the surface with time.

The processing algorithm starts from scratch with the base velocity product. At each elevation, and range, it examines all of the bins throughout the entire azimuth sweep to find groups of adjacent bins that show an increase or decrease in velocity from one end to the other. The change must span a large enough number of bins to be counted. This value is called the "pattern vector threshold" and can be modified by the radar operator. If the change exceeds the pattern vector threshold, typically ten bins, and meets a threshold value of shear and momentum, the change is classified as a pattern vector.

The MDA tries to link all pattern vectors to form two-dimensional features. When this is completed, it attempts to resolve these features into three-dimensional circulations by linking the features to others at higher elevations.

Based on the success of this three-dimensional correlation, the feature is then identified as one of three things: three-dimensional uncorrelated shear, uncorrelated shear, or a mesocyclone. Three-dimensional uncorrelated shear has vertical but not horizontal consistency. Uncorrelated shear is the opposite; it has horizontal consistency but none in the vertical. A mesocyclone, however, contains both. Finally the MDA creates an attribute table showing each feature, its type, location, and identification number.

The algorithm was initially developed for powerful Great Plains supercells, however a series of refinements in the mid-1990s allowed better performance at radar sites nationwide.

- Much of the work at the National Severe Storms Laboratory during the early 1980s focused on developing an accurate Mesocyclone Detection Algorithm.

- A Mesocyclone Overlay feature should persist for at least two volume scans to be considered a temporally consistent feature.

- No radar providers on the Internet are known to offer mesocyclone overlays at this time. Implementation into a Digital Atmosphere release is planned for autumn 2003.

- Anticyclonic shear is not detected by the MDA.

- The biggest shortfall of the Mesocyclone Detection Algorithm is set by the radar's range and beam width. Beyond 60 nm, the beam widens too much to adequately resolve shear features. All features within 5.4 nm are not processed as they are too close.

- All Mesocyclone Detection Algorithm features are dependent on the accuracy of the base velocity data. Range folding, dealiasing problems, and other anomalies can produce false or spurious indications.

- In 1995, a series of NOAA internal memos encouraged radar operators to change the pattern vector threshold from 10 to a lower number to allow greater sensitivity to smaller shear features.

- The product code is 60/M.

Great sites with real-time data for this product . . .
○ None are known to exist at this time.

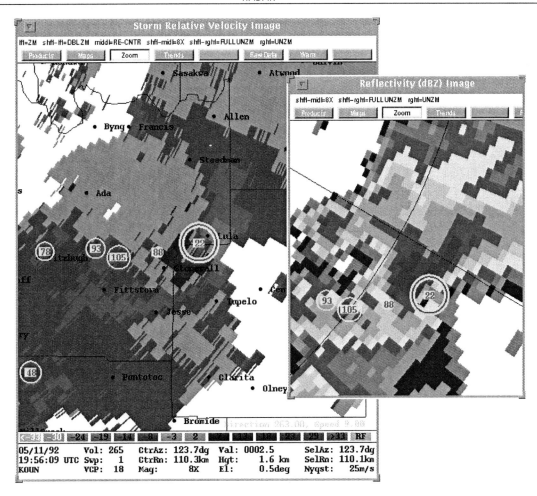

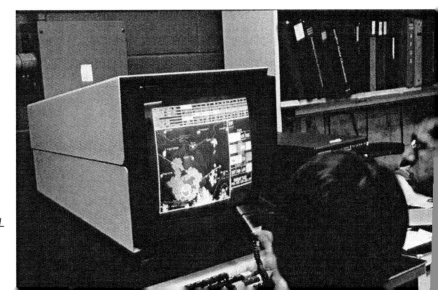

Above: NSSL demonstrator display of the mesocyclone algorithm. Each area of uncorrelated shear is identified by a yellow circle, with a mesocyclone circled by both yellow and red. *(NSSL)*

Right: Much of the work on NEXRAD algorithms took place at the National Severe Storms Laboratory. Here a mesocyclone tracking algorithm is being tested around the mid or late 1980s. *(NSSL photo)*

Tornadic Vortex Signature (TVS)

When NEXRAD units were first fielded, they were equipped with the Tornadic Vortex Signature (TVS) algorithm. The algorithm was developed by the National Severe Storms Laboratories in the mid-1980s. It was dependent on the Mesocyclone Algorithm and looked for velocity couplets in identified mesocyclones which exceeded a threshold value. Unfortunately it was not very flexible and often missed weaker tornadoes.

The Tornado Detection Algorithm (TDA) was developed by the National Severe Storms Laboratory as a replacement. It was included in Build 10 of NEXRAD, which was released in November 1998. The TDA came with its own logic to scrutinize the entire radial velocity product, freeing it from the dependence on the Mesocyclone Algorithm. Although the new TVS algorithm is called the TDA, the end-user product is still called "TVS" to this day.

Much like the Mesocyclone Detection Algorithm, the TDA builds one-dimensional pattern vectors, then two-dimensional features, then three-dimensional circulations. It then uses altitude, depth, and shear criteria to identify possible tornadoes. TDA actually examines the pattern vectors to calculate shear, rather than finding couplets. At least three features are required with a depth of at least 1.5 km, must have a base at 0.5 deg or below 600 meters, whichever is lower, and must have a low-level velocity differential of 49 kt or a maximum velocity differential of 70 kt.

An Elevated TVS (ETVS) is the same but may be above 0.5 deg and 600 meters and requires only a low-level velocity differential of 49 kt. It generally indicates sharp rotation aloft and ideally will alert forecasters to a developing tornado.

When scrutinizing a TDA TVS, consider whether the atmosphere is capable of providing the instability and shear neccessary for a tornado. False alarms do occur. Also note that at ranges beyond 35 nm the TDA may be triggered by strong mesocyclones.

In closing, it must be emphasized that the TDA product, as well as other algorithms, are not the holy grail of tornado detection. The forecaster must interrogate all available data, including radar images and spotter reports, and produce a coherent picture of what is happening. This must be weighed against one's own experience and in context with sound meteorological principles. Only then can a tornado forecast be considered robust and impeccable.

Great sites with real-time data for this product . . .
○ None are known to exist at this time.

■ The TDA (Tornado Detection Algorithm) is the updated version of the TVS (Tornadic Vortex Signature) algorithm.

■ The purpose of this algorithm is not just to detect a tornado, but to attempt to provide forecasters with a 10-minute lead time and provide important guidance to weather warning operations.

■ The standard symbol for a non-elevated tornadic vortex signature (TVS) is a filled triangle that points downward.

■ The standard symbol for an elevated tornadic vortex signature (ETVS) is an open triangle that points downward.

■ The location of the TVS/ETVS signature is at the location of the shear at the lowest elevation; in other words, where it should be on the ground, if at all.

■ The TVS and TDA algorithms do not detect anticyclonic shear, and thus will not detect the very rare anticyclonic tornado.

■ The original Tornadic Vortex Signature (TVS) algorithm was not very flexible, and actual tornadoes were often missed. The TDA algorithm is better, but is somewhat more complex, produces its share of false alarm ratios, and has parameters that need more research.

■ The product code is 61/TVS.

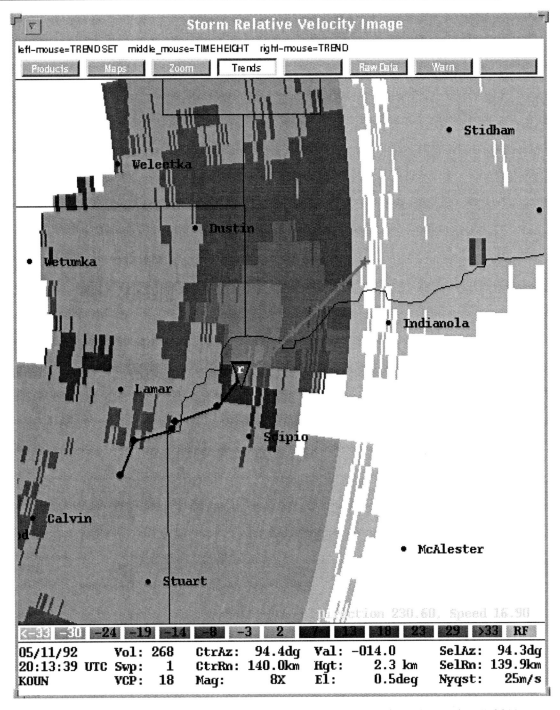

Above: Prototype display of the TVS algorithm at NSSL shows a confirmed tornado. *(NSSL)*

VAD Wind Profile (VWP)

The Velocity Azimuth Display (VAD) Wind Profile (VWP) displays a time-height diagram of wind direction and speed. The data is derived from base velocity data. VWP data is provided every 1,000 ft from 1,000 to 70,000 ft MSL. The data is color coded to show the root mean square error in knots, which is inversely proportional to the reliability of the data at that height.

The VAD algorithm first waits for all reflectivity and velocity data to be processed, dealiased, and range unfolded. It then sequentially figures a wind speed at each height level. It does this by finding the scan elevation and range closest to a distance called the VAD Analysis Range or VAD Optimum Slant Range (usually 18.6 nm), which is a direct distance to the scatterer rather than a horizontal range. The algorithm analyzes all of the scatterers at that range and elevation on a sweep of all azimuths.

If 25 scatterers are detected, the algorithm attempts to fit a sine wave to the azimuth and velocity of all the data points. The sine wave configuration is used because an ideal plot of winds that are constant throughout the scan volume will resemble a sine wave if the velocity is plotted with respect to azimuth. Therefore the data should fit this curve.

The processor checks the fit of the data to the sine wave by computing a root mean square (RMS) error. This determines the reliability of the entire sample. A symmetry analysis is then done by comparing the departure of the fitted curve's baseline (zero-velocity line) from that of a standard sine wave. If the data fails the analysis by not meeting either check it is discarded and the data is considered void at that level.

During convective weather situations, changes in the low levels of the atmosphere may show important trends in storm-relative helicity. Also strengthening of upper-level flow may hint at upper-level dynamics and increasing bulk shear moving into the threat area.

The VWP may indicate coupling or decoupling of the boundary layer, especially at night or during the morning. This is most obvious when lower-tropospheric winds remain constant but winds in the lowest 1 to 2 thousand feet drop to calm after dark or increase to match the lower-tropospheric winds during the morning.

Also frontal inversions can be assessed using the VWP product, signified by two layers with markedly different wind regimes. The VWP can reveal the depth and character of the cold air mass.

■ VWP shows a profile plot of winds aloft very much like wind profiler systems. However the sample is volumetric, covering a region nearly 200 miles wide, and so important features may be smoothed over. Another significant difference is the VWP requires more scatterers than wind profilers.

■ VWP requires a significant number of scatterers to work. The best scatterers are produced by dust, insects, and cloud droplets. If scatterers are not present, a data void will occur. This is quite common, especially during good weather.

■ Bad data will be produced by birds, air mass boundaries, and thunderstorms. This will reflect velocity signatures that differ from the mean wind at that level. It may increase the RMS error at that level or cause it to be rejected altogether. Use the results with extreme caution when any of these are suspected.

■ A RMS error of over 9.7 kt or a symmetry error of over 13.6 kt will invalidate the data for that level.

■ For a given level, the highest amplitude of the VWP sine wave is considered to be the wind speed, while the phase of the highest inbound amplitude is considered to be the wind direction.

■ A void will occur when any data sample fails the VWP algorithm.

■ The product code is 48/VWP.

Great sites with real-time data for this product . . .
○ CoD — **weather.cod.edu/analysis/radar.main.html**
○ NWS — **www.nws.noaa.gov/radar**
○ Weathertap ($) — **www.weathertap.com**

VAD Wind Profile (VWP).

This graph shows wind speed and direction as a function of altitude (Y) and time (X). In this example, the column on the far right represents the most current observation. Winds are southwesterly at 25 to 35 kt near the surface and 20 to 50 kt in the upper troposphere. It can be seen that a layer of scatterers at about 35,000 ft is deepening rapidly with time, suggesting a deep cirrus layer (probably from a thunderstorm) invading the region. Indeed, these charts can sometimes be used to determine the height and thickness of stratiform cloud layers.

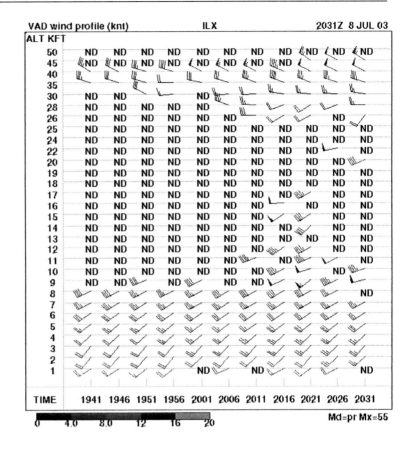

Velocity Azimuth Display.

Not to be confused with a Velocity Wind Profile (VWP), this is what a velocity azimuth display really looks like. It is a graph of azimuth (X) versus velocity (Y) at a given height, in this case 13,000 ft. This is a primitive radar product and is unlikely to be found on the Internet since a single volume scan could generate dozens of these graphs. However it serves a useful example by showing the sine wave and data points from which a VWP product is constructed.

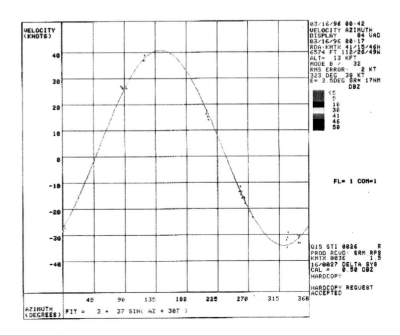

Free Text Message

The radar is down. Fine, but how do you find out what the cause was and when it is expected to be back up? What if there is some important change in the operating parameters you need to know about Fortunately the WSR-88D designers had a plan in mind: the Free Text Message (FTM).

This product is available for all radar sites, and it gives radar operators the ability to post public information pertinent to the radar. This reaches the hands of not only hobbyists and media forecasters, but also air traffic control centers, other weather offices, and the NOAA Radar Operations Center. It also allows the operators to post expected stop and start times, which are required as prescribed by Federal Meteorological Hanbook standards, if an outage occurs or is scheduled.

During the early and mid-1990s when the system was slower and loadshedding was occurring, the Free Text Message allowed operators to send out a status message. It would usually encourage users to cut back on product requests.http://www.emc.ncep.noaa.gov/mmb/papers/collins/preprints/vadqc.htm

At National Weather Service offices, the Free Text Message is entered either at the Unit Control Position (UCP) or at a Master System Control Function (MSCF) workstation.

A useful link to check the status of a radar is at <weather.noaa.gov/monitor/radar>. The page contains a list of all radars color-coded by latency of data, and with a full listing of all Free Text Messages. The page automatically updates every 60 seconds.

> ■ Free Text Messages (also sometimes called Status Messages) reveal important information about outages, defective equipment, and other conditions that may affect the radar unit.
>
> ■ The product code is 75/FTM.
>
> ■ If your Web radar service does not provide Free Text Messages, ask for them!

Great sites with real-time data for this product . . .
○ CoD — **weather.cod.edu/analysis/radar.main.html**
○ NWS — **www.nws.noaa.gov/radar**
○ Weathertap ($) — **www.weathertap.com**

```
NOUS65 KBOI 041143
FTMCBX

MESSAGE DATE: AUG 4 2003 5:40 AM MDT

STORM TOTAL PRECIPITATION IS RESET TO ZERO AS A RESULT OF
SWITCHING THE RADAR TO CLEAR AIR MODE EARLY THIS MONDAY
MORNING. THE NEXT PRECIPITATION EVENT IS ON TAP FOR LATE
THIS AFTERNOON OR EVENING THROUGH TUESDAY NIGHT.
```

WSR_88D OUTAGE NOTIFICATION
NATIONAL WEATHER SERVICE SAN ANGELO TX
1022 PM CDT MON AUG 4 2003

ATTENTION NCF...FWD...MAF...LBB...EWX...SRH ROC
THE KSJT...SAN ANGELO...RADAR WILL REMAIN IN STANDBY MODE OVERNIGHT.
FAULTY AIR-CONDITION UNITS ARE RESULTING IN EXTREMELY HIGH EQUIPMENT
SHELTER TEMPERATURES. DUNCAN AND DUNCAN...OUR LOCAL AIR CONDITIONING
SPECIALISTS...WILL ADDRESS THE PROBLEM EARLY TUESDAY MORNING. THE
KDYX...DYESS AFB...RADAR IS OPERATIONAL.

NOUS61 KOKX 041407
FTMOKX

DUE TO THE DEEP-LAYERED MOISTURE...KOKX RADAR HAS SWITCHED TO THE
TROPICAL Z/R R ELATIONSHIP.

NOUS62 KCHS 021340
FTMCLX

WSR-88D NOTIFICATION MESSAGE
NATIONAL WEATHER SERVICE CHARLESTON SC
940 AM EDT SAT AUG 2 2003

TO ALL USERS OF KCLX RADAR DATA:

THE KCLX RADAR IS BACK ONLINE BUT IT CONTINUES TO HAVE PROBLEMS.
RANGE RINGS CAUSING HIGH REFLECTIVITY RETURNS CONTINUE TO APPEAR ON
RADAR PRODUCTS. THE KCLX RADAR WILL CONTINUE TO HAVE THIS PROBLEM AS
WE AWAIT ARRIVAL OF THE ESA. PARTS ARE ALSO ON ORDER. LOCAL
TROUBLESHOOTING PROCEDURES HAVE SO FAR BEEN UNABLE TO EVEN
TEMPORARILY CORRECT THE PROBLEM. RANGE RINGS WILL CONTINUE AT LEAST
UNTIL THE ESA ARRIVES.

WE APOLOGIZE FOR ANY INCONVENIENCES THIS MAY CAUSE TO KCLX USERS.

ADJACENT WSR-88DS...KLTX...KCAE...KJGX...KVAX...KJAX.

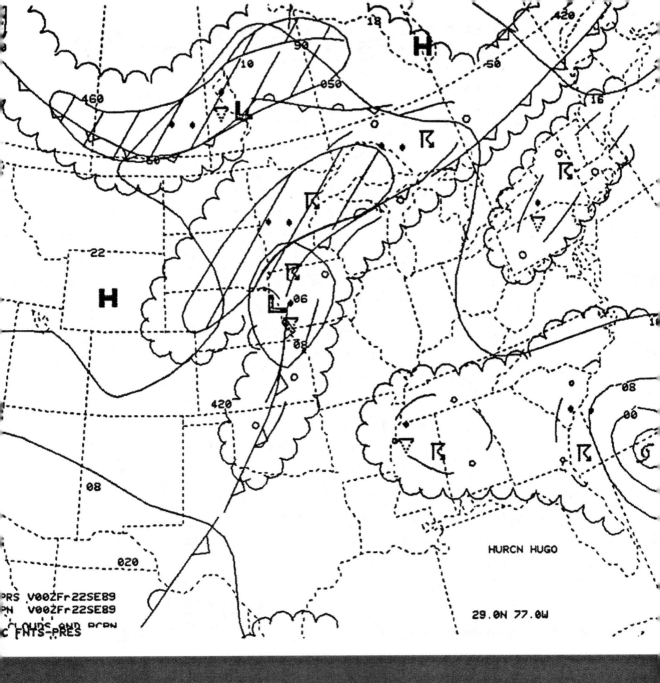

HURCN HUGO

29.0N 77.0W

PRS VØØZFr22SE89
PN VØØZFr22SE89
CLOUDS AND PCPN
C FHTS-PRES

HUMAN FORECASTS

Above: AFOS was the high-tech graphical workstation in all National Weather Service offices from the 1980s until the mid-1990s. Seen here is an NCEP forecast dating to 1989.

SPC Convective Outlook

The Convective Outlook is an official forecast transmitted four times a day which establishes the threat of severe thunderstorms across the United States. It is created by a qualified team of thunderstorm forecasters operating within a special branch of the National Oceanic and Atmospheric Administration: the Storm Prediction Center (SPC). The product was first transmitted by the Severe Local Storms unit (SELS) in 1955 and by fax in 1961 from Kansas City.

Currently, a vast array of observational data and models are used to develop the convective outlook. This is comprised of every forecasting tool available, including surface and upper air observations, profiler data, satellite data, and RUC, Eta, and MM5 model output.

The categories of severe weather risk are as follows.

■ **General.** There is a 10-percent or better chance of thunderstorms.

■ **Slight risk** (SLGT). Well-organized severe thunderstorms are expected but in small numbers and/or coverage. Verification is made up of either 5 to 29 reports of 1-inch or larger hail, and/or 3 to 5 tornadoes, and/or 5 to 29 wind events.

■ **Moderate risk** (MDT). Great concentration of severe storms. Verification is made up of either 30 or more reports of 1-inch or larger hail, and/or 6 to 19 tornadoes, and/or 30 or more wind events.

■ **High risk** (HIGH). A major severe weather outbreak. At least 20 tornadoes are expected with at least two producing F3 damage or an extreme derecho event with widespread wind damage.

Convective outlooks come not only with a map but also with an informative text bulletin. It defines the reasoning behind the outlook and provides a brief overview of what is expected to unfold. The outlook coordinates included in the bulletin allow human plotters and machines to duplicate the bulletin's coordinate information.

SPC's products narrow down to two other types of products when the event draws closer. The Mesoscale Discussion (MCD) is disseminated when conditions appear to be favorable for severe thunderstorm development within the next three hours. Finally, when a public advisory is required and severe weather is imminent, a severe thunderstorm or tornado watch is issued. It generally has a lifespan of four to six hours. Watch boxes with a high risk of severe weather are called PDS watches ("particularly dangerous situation"), a contraction for the terminology that is written into the watch's summary.

Great sites with real-time data for this product . . .
○ SPC — **www.spc.noaa.gov/products/outlook**

■ The Storm Prediction Center (SPC) was known as the National Severe Storms Forecast Center (NSSFC) until 1995. This closely coincided with its move from Kansas City, Missouri to Norman, Oklahoma, which took place in 1997.

■ The first Day 2 Outlook was disseminated in 1986. In this year the first Mesoscale Discussion was issued.

■ Convective outlooks were only sent during the morning until 1974, when an afternoon outlook was added during the warm season.

■ SPC issues watches and outlooks. It does not issue warnings. These are the responsibility of local weather service forecast offices.

■ SPC issues approximately 1,000 watches per year.

■ Convective outlook text is very educational in nature and reveals the thought process behind a thunderstorm forecast. It serves as an excellent model for novice forecasters to study.

■ In a progressive flow pattern with well-defined surface systems, there is a tendency for the western edge of a moderate or high risk area to carry the threat early in the period, with the eastern edge getting the action later in the period. The outlook text will usually elaborate on this further.

■ Storm chasers usually consider a Moderate Risk as an optimal situation for photogenic tornadoes. A High Risk often implies linear, fast-moving modes and squall lines, while a Low Risk often indicates a missing ingredient from an ideal situation.

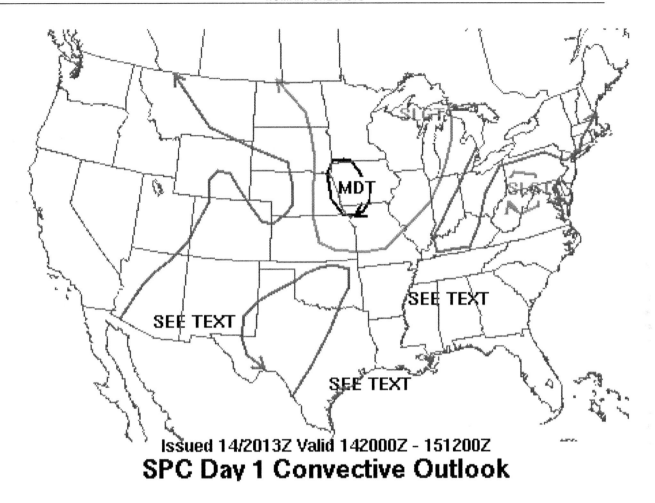

Issued 14/2013Z Valid 142000Z - 151200Z

SPC Day 1 Convective Outlook

Above: A sample convective outlook for 14 July 2003. It reveals a substantial threat of severe weather in western Iowa.

Right: Forecasting floor at the Storm Prediction Center, as seen during a graveyard shift at 1 am. *(Tim Vasquez)*

HPC Surface Prognosis

The Hydrometeorological Prediction Center (HPC) in Camp Springs, Maryland assumes much of the centralized forecast guidance for United States weather offices. It came into being in late 1995 with the reorganization of the National Meteorological Center (NMC) into the National Centers for Environmental Prediction (NCEP). The main objectives of HPC are to provide quantitative precipitation forecasts, medium-range public forecasts, numerical model diagnostics and discussions, surface analysis responsibilities, and an international desk for visiting meteorologists.

The national forecast graphics are a useful chart for forecasters who want a quick summary of expected weather across the nation. The graphics also provide excellent information on the expected transition lines between rain and snow.

The "Basic Weather" forecaster is responsible for the preparation of the 12-48 hour forecasts. They are issued twice a day, and their primary purpose is to accurately depict the evolution of major weather systems that will affect the United States.

The medium range forecast products, extending out to 7 days, are prepared by a team of two meteorologists twice a day. One forecaster focuses on weather systems and fronts while the other concentrates on precipitation and temperatures. A preliminary graphic is released to National Weather Service offices at 10 am EST for coordination purposes, with the public release occurring at 2 pm EST.

- HPC is a NCEP service center, which makes it a sister facility of the Storm Prediction Center, the Tropical Prediction Center, the Climate Prediction Center, and the Aviation Weather Center.

- The HPC prognosis charts are human-made and incorporate a blend of model guidance and forecaster experience.

- The prognosis charts are "instantaneous" graphics, therefore the movement of weather systems and precipitation areas must be considered in between valid time periods.

- The forecast charts had been transmitted via DIFAX circuits for well over 20 years. The charts adopted an electronic format during the 1980s, and the fax version was discontinued on 15 January 2003.

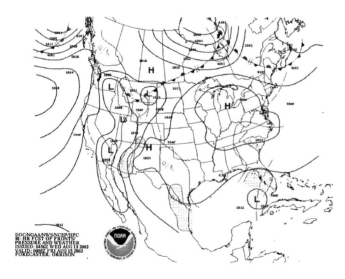

Left: A 48-hour forecast panel.

Above right: Short-range 12-hour forecast produced by HPC.

Below right: Long-range 7-day forecast with accompanying forecast discussion (AWIPS bulletin NFDPMDEPD or FOS bulletin FXUS02 KWBC).

Great sites with real-time data for this product . . .
○ HPC — www.hpc.ncep.noaa.gov/basicwx/basicwx.shtml

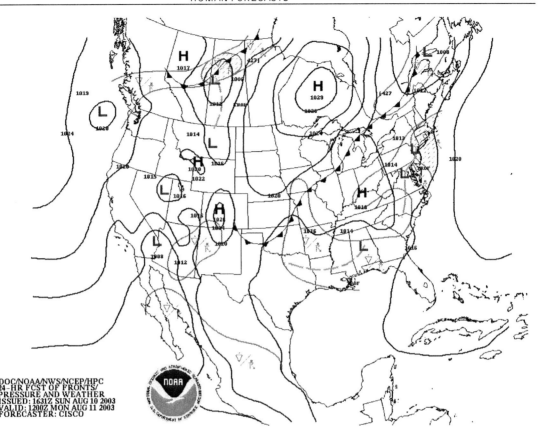

DOC/NOAA/NWS/NCEP/HPC
24-HR FCST OF FRONTS/
PRESSURE AND WEATHER
ISSUED: 1631Z SUN AUG 10 2003
VALID: 1200Z MON AUG 11 2003
FORECASTER: CISCO

EXTENDED FORECAST DISCUSSION
NWS HYDROMETEOROLOGICAL PREDICTION CENTER
CAMP SPRINGS MD
231 PM EDT SUN AUG 10 2003
VALID 12Z WED AUG 13 2003 - 12Z SUN AUG 17 2003
...FINAL MEDIUM RANGE DISCUSSION....
...MODEL DISCUSSION... ...
PATTERN OVERVIEW AND MODEL DISCUSSION FOR
CONUS...
SOME CHANGES APPEAR ON THE HORIZON AS THE
ANOMALOUS UPPER TROF OVER THE ERN STATES SPLITS
APART WITH THE SRN PORTION DRIFTING WWD TO THE
SRN PLAINS. THE NRN PORTION OF THE TROF OVER THE
ST LAWRENCE SEAWAY WILL FILL AS HEIGHTS BUILD
OVER THE GREAT LAKES REGION BY MIDWEEK. BUT
THESE CHANGES MAY ONLY BE TEMPORARY. BY NEXT
WEEKEND...THE D+8 GFS SHOWS SIGNS OF A RETURN
TO A FLATTER TROF-RIDGE-TROF LONGWAVE PATTERN
FROM THE ERN PACIFIC ACROSS NOAM. IN
CONTRAST...THE ECMWF D+8 SHOWS BROAD CYCLONIC
FLOW ACROSS THE GULF OF ALASKA AND RATHER
ZONAL FLOW ACROSS SRN CANADA....WITH A
LINGERING FLAT RIDGE OVER THE ERN CONUS. THE
SHORT-TERM HEIGHT RISES OVER THE LAKES AREA ARE
FAVORED BY TWO OTHER FEATURES IN THE GENERAL
CIRCULATION. THE VERY DEEP UPPER SYS OVER THE

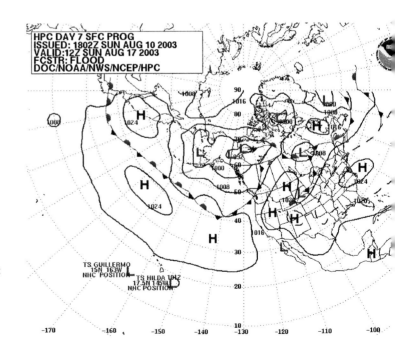

HPC DAY 7 SFC PROG
ISSUED: 1802Z SUN AUG 10 2003
VALID:12Z SUN AUG 17 2003
FCSTR: FLOOD
DOC/NOAA/NWS/NCEP/HPC

Area Forecast Discussion (AFD)

There is probably no better insight into a National Weather Service forecaster's mind than the Area Forecast Discussion (AFD). These bulletins are composed before a forecast package is issued, typically twice a day with updates two more times per day.

The AFD was known as an SFD (State Forecast Discussion) before a restructuring initiative in the mid-1990s. It is also sometimes known as an FP, or FPUS3 bulletin, taking this name from its assigned header under the Family of Services (FOS) distribution circuit.

For decades the forecast discussion bulletin used a vast number of contractions. This characteristic carried over from the 1970s when data circuits were slow and brevity was valued. During the mid-1990s most offices began transitioning to plain English format. However, contractions are still frequently encountered, and they may be decoded with the guide below.

Great sites with real-time data for this product . . .
❍ NWS IWIN — **iwin.nws.noaa.gov**

■ The Area Forecast Discussion (AFD) is designed to allow the forecaster to explain their forecast thinking to other meteorologists, to weather-sensitive officials, and to interested members of the public.

■ The AFD is often used by broadcast meteorologists for an inside scoop on NWS thinking.

■ The bulletin text is followed either by the forecaster's last name or a numerical code that refers to the forecaster.

■ A survey of 188 AFD users in 2001 by the Gaylord, Michigan WSFO showed that 69% were weather enthusiasts and 14% broadcasters.

FORECAST DISCUSSION CONTRACTIONS

ABNDT abundant	CDFNT cold front	FQT frequent	LFTG lifting	NGM nested grid model	PVL prevail
ABT about	CG cloud to ground	FRM form	LGRNG long range	NGT night	QPF quantitative
ABV above	CHC chance	FROPA frontal passage	LGWV long wave	NIL none	precipitation forecast
AC convective outlook	CI cirrus	FRZN frozen	LI lifted index	NLY northerly	RCV receive
ACLT accelerate	CIG ceiling	FT terminal forecast	LIS lifted indices	NNNN end of message	RGL regional model
ACPY accompany	CNTY county	FWD forward	LK lake	NRLY nearly	RGN region
ACTV active	COR correction	GEN general	LKLY likely	NTFY notify	RNFL rainfall
ADJ adjacent	CPBL capable	GND ground	LLJ low level jet	NVA negative vorticity	ROT rotate
ADL additional	CRNR corner	GRDL gradual	LMTD limited	advection	RPLC replace
ADVCT advect	CSDRBL considerable	GRT great	LN line	NXT next	RSG rising
ADVN advance	CST coast	HAZ hazard	LRG large	OBND outbound	SA surface observation
ADVY advisory	DBL double	HGT height	LST local standard time	OBS observation	SCT scatter/scattered
ACFTG affecting	DCR decrease	HLF half	LTD limited	OBSC obscure	SEPN separation
AFT after	DFNT definite	HLSTO hailstones	LTG lightning	OCLD occlude	SGFNT significant
AFTN afternoon	DISC discussion	HV have	LTL little	OCNL occasional	SKC sky clear
ALG along	DLA delay	HVY heavy	LYR layer	OCR occur	SLP slope or pressure
ALQDS all quadrants	DLT delete	HWY highway	MAX maximum	OFC office	SPRD spread
AMD amend	DMG damage	IC ice	MDFY modify	OFP occluded frontal	SR sunrise
AMS air mass	DPND deepened	IMDT immediate	MDL model	passage	SS sunset
AMT amount	DSCNT descent	IMPL impulse	MDT moderate	OMTNS over	STFR stratus fractus
ANAL analysis	DSIPT dissipate	INCL include	MED medium	mountains	SX stability index
AOA at or above	DURG during	INCR increase	MEGG merging	OTLK outlook	TNTV tentative
AOB at or below	DVLP develop	INDC indicate	MESO mesoscale	OTP on top	TROF trough
APRNT apparent	DVRG diverge	INDEF indefinitely	MET meteorological	OTR other	TS thunderstorm
ARPT airport	DVRGG diverging	INSTBY instability	MID middle	OTRW otherwise	UPR upper
ATTM at this time	DVV downward motion	INTS intense	MISG missing	OVC overcast	UVV upward motion
AWT awaiting	EBND eastbound	IOVC in overcast	MOV move	OVTK overtake	VC vicinity
BCM become	ELNGTD elongated	INVOF in vicinityof	MRGL marginal	PBL boundary layer	VFR visual flight rules
BD blowing dust	EMBDD embedded	IPV improve	MRNG morning	PCPN precipitation	VRG veering
BDRY boundary	ERN eastern	ISOL isolate	MSG message	PLNS plains	VV vertical velocity
BFR before	ERY easterly	ISOLD isolated	MSL mean sea level	POS positive	WAA warm advection
BLD build	ETA Eta model	KFRST killing frost	MST most	PRST persist	WKN weaken
BLO below	EWD eastward	KT knots	MXD mixed	PSBL possible	WTR water
BYD beyond	FA aviation forecast	LAT latitude	NAB not above	PTLY partly	WX weather
CAA cold air advection	FLRY flurry	LCL local	NBND northbound	PVA positive vorticity	YDA yesterday
CCLDS clear of clouds	FLW follow	LCTMP little temp chg	NEG negative	advection	ZN zone

FXUS65 KFGZ 130958
AFDFLG

NORTHERN ARIZONA FORECAST DISCUSSION
NATIONAL WEATHER SERVICE FLAGSTAFF AZ
255 AM MST WED AUG 13 2003

.SYNOPSIS...THE AIR MASS OVER ARIZONA WILL REMAIN MOIST AND UNSTABLE
THIS WEEK. AFTERNOON AND EVENING SHOWERS WILL DEVELOP EACH
DAY. THE STORMS WILL BECOME MORE NUMEROUS ON THURSDAY AS A LOW
PRESSURE SYSTEM MOVES INTO THE STATE. LOOK FOR COOLER TEMPERATURES
AND DAILY THUNDERSTORM DEVELOPMENT THROUGH THE WEEKEND.

.DISCUSSION...THE HIGH PRESSURE SYSTEM OVER THE STATE CONTINUES TO
ELONGATE WITH THE AXIS SW-NE AS THE CENTER DRIFTS TOWARD THE
NORTHERN PLAINS. SW FLOW ALOFT HAS BROUGHT MID LEVEL DRYING TO THE
WESTERN CWA. GPSMET IPWV DATA SHOWS DRYING OVER THE LAST 7 HRS WITH
FLG PW CURRENTLY DOWN TO 0.50 INCHES. SOUTHERN AZ REMAINS VERY MOIST
WITH PW'S NEAR 1.5 INCHES. BEST CHANCE OF CONVECTION TODAY IS OVER
THE EASTERN CWA WHERE EQUIV POT TEMP AXIS...LOWEST LI'S AND DEEPEST
MOISTURE RESIDES.

WX PATTERN CHANGES SIGNIFICANTLY STARTING ON THURSDAY. HI PRESSURE
OVER THE STATE RETREATS NORTHWARD AS CLOSED LOW CURRENTLY OVER TX
MOVES TO THE AZ/NM BORDER. DIVQ FIELDS INDICATE INCREASED LIFT OVER
THE CWA THURSDAY ALONG WITH EQUIV POT TEMP AXIS ACROSS THE NORTHERN
CWA...GOOD INSTABILITY AND PW RISING TO OVER ONE INCH. EXPECT TO SEE
AN ACTIVE DAY WITH THE POTENTIAL FOR HEAVY RAINFALL AMOUNTS...
ESPECIALLY OVER THE FLASH FLOOD PRONE AREAS OF THE WESTERN CWA.
COOL AND UNSTABLE WX ON TAP FOR FRIDAY AS THE STATE REMAINS UNDER
THE LOW PRESSURE INVERTED TROF. DYNAMICS WEAKER BUT STILL SHOULD SEE
SCT POPS ACROSS THE CWA.

EXTENDED...AN AREA OF LOW PRESSURE WILL LINGER OVER THE STATE THRU
THE WEEKEND. EXPECT A CHANCE OF SHOWERS AND TSTMS TO DEVELOP EACH
DAY. EARLY NEXT WEEK HIGH PRESSURE REBUILDS INTO THE REGION FROM
THE EAST. THEN THE REGION IS BACK TO A MORE NORMAL MONSOON PATTERN
WITH DAILY CHANCE OF CONVECTION CONTINUING. DF

.FGZ...NONE.

```
-  CALCULATE QDOT                                                                SOLVE.2
                                                                                 SOLVE.2
-  SIGMADOT=-RHO.G.W/PS-SIG/PS.DPSDX.U-SIG/PS.DPSDY.V                             SOLVE.28
                                                                                 SOLVE.2
       DO K=2,KL                                                                 SOLVE.2
         DO I=1,ILX                                                              SOLVE.2
           RHOOS=TWT(K,1)*RHOO(I,J,K)+TWT(K,2)*RHOO(I,J,K-1)                     SOLVE.2
           QDOT(I,J,K)=-RHOOS*G*W3D(I,J,K)*RPSA(I,J)*0.001                       SOLVE.2
     +               -SIGMA(K)*(DPSDXM(I,J)*(TWT(K,1)*UCC(I,J,K)                 SOLVE.2
     +                                     +TWT(K,2)*UCC(I,J,K-1))               SOLVE.2
     +                        +DPSDYM(I,J)*(TWT(K,1)*VCC(I,J,K)                  SOLVE.2
     +                                     +TWT(K,2)*VCC(I,J,K-1)))              SOLVE.2
         ENDDO                                                                   SOLVE.2
       ENDDO                                                                     SOLVE.2
                                                                                 SOLVE.2
-  CALCULATE TOTAL DIVERGENCE AND STORE IN DIVX                                  SOLVE.293
                                                                                 SOLVE.2
       DO I=1,ILX                                                                SOLVE.2
         DUMMY(I)=1.0/(DX2*MSFX(I,J)*MSFX(I,J))                                  SOLVE.2
       ENDDO                                                                     SOLVE.2
                                                                                 SOLVE.2
       DO K=1,KL                                                                 SOLVE.2
         DO I=1,ILX                                                              SOLVE.3
           DIV=UA(I+1,J+1,K)+UA(I,J+1,K)-UA(I+1,J,K)-UA(I,J,K)+                  SOLVE.3
     +         VA(I+1,J+1,K)+VA(I+1,J,K)-VA(I,J+1,K)-VA(I,J,K)                   SOLVE.3
           DIVX(I,J,K)=DIV*DUMMY(I)+(QDOT(I,J,K+1)-QDOT(I,J,K))*                 SOLVE.3
     +                 PSA(I,J)/DSIGMA(K)                                        SOLVE.3
         ENDDO                                                                   SOLVE.3
       ENDDO                                                                     SOLVE.3
     ENDDO                                                                       SOLVE.3
                                                                                 SOLVE.3
*** COMPUTE HORIZONTAL ADVECTION TERMS FOR U, V, PP, W:                          SOLVE.3
                                                                                 SOLVE.3
     CALL HADV(KZZ,U3DTEN,UA,VA,U3D,MSFD,DX16,3,INEST)                           SOLVE.3
     CALL HADV(KZZ,V3DTEN,UA,VA,V3D,MSFD,DX16,3,INEST)                           SOLVE.3
     CALL HADV(KZZ,PP3DTEN,UA,VA,PP3D,MSFX,DX4,1,INEST)                          SOLVE.3
     CALL HADV(KZZ+1,W3DTEN,UA,VA,W3D,MSFX,DX4,4,INEST)                          SOLVE.3
                                                                                 SOLVE.3
*** COMPUTE VERTICAL ADVECTION TERMS FOR U, V, PP, W:
```

NUMERICAL WEATHER PREDICTION

Above: Part of the source code for the MM5 mesoscale model, written in FORTRAN. *(Courtesy UCAR)*

Numerical Weather Prediction

Numerical weather prediction is the science of predicting the future state of the atmosphere using physical equations. The technique was first proposed in 1923 by Lewis Frye Richardson, a British meteorologist, in his book *Weather Prediction by Numerical Process*. Unfortunately, the technology and resources were simply not available at the time to pursue the idea.

With the breakthroughs in computing technology during the 1950s, researchers had fantastic opportunities for laying down the craft of numerical weather prediction. Universities and government institutions worked together to develop simple barotropic models, which became more sophisticated as scientific knowledge grew. The first operational predictions were available by 1960, and were followed by fantastic leaps and bounds in the decades ahead.

What is a numerical model?

While the physics and dynamics of models are far beyond the scope of this book, it is most important to point out that each model runs at a unique scale. Depending on the weather agency and purpose, a model is either run at a coarse resolution covering the entire world, or is run at a fine resolution covering a small area (usually the agency's home continent). The worldwide model is called a "global" model, while the fine model is called a "regional" model. Even finer models covering smaller areas, such as portions of a country, are called "mesoscale" models.

Detailed models are very accurate but are limited by their enormous processing requirements, which limits them to a specific area of the globe. As a result they suffer from boundary errors on their edges and their forecasts begin degrading just one or two days into the future. During the first day or two, forecasters are encouraged to use the regional models for their greater detail, but past this point should use global models, which lack boundary errors.

Forecasters must also be aware of the unique characteristics of each model, which are detailed section by section in this book, where applicable. These can range from eccentricities in the parameterization of radiation and convection, which show up in unusual ways, to shortfalls in vertical and horizontal resolution which give the model weaknesses in certain weather regimes. All of these are referred to as *model biases*.

When the hemispheric wave number, the number of long waves around a hemisphere, undergoes a change, it is referred to as a *wave number transition*. A common example is when a low wave number suddenly increases from 2 or 3 to 5 or 6 over one to two days. One signal of a possible pending transition is when a very strong, long, broad polar jet becomes established in the North Pacific Ocean. Transition events signal a major shift in weather regimes, and are notorious for causing errors and inconsistencies in numerical weather forecasts. Always be wary of forecasts beyond 48 hours when a wave number transition is suspected or is underway.

Getting model data

There are three primary sources of model data graphics on the Internet: government, academic, and commercial. The exception is "link sites", which contain no original content and simply refer to one of the sources below. Though they may be handy for navigating to

NCEP Computing Power

Year	Model	Processors	Operational Speed (Mflops)	Memory (MB)	Disk storage	Operational Model
1956	IBM 701	1	**0.001**	0.001	9 KB	(Research)
1958	IBM 704	1	**0.008**	0.02	144 KB	Barotropic
1960	IBM 7090	1	**0.067**	0.1	5-50 MB	3-lvl QG model
1963	IBM 7094	1	**0.1**	0.1	5-50 MB	Baroclinic
1966	CDC 6600	1	**3**	1	75 MB	6-lvl PE, LFM
1974	IBM 360/195	1	**10**	4	300 MB	LFM, 7-lvl PE
1978	CDC Cyber 205	1	**100**	32	7.2 GB	OI, GSM, NGM
1987	CDC Cyber 205	2	**200**	64	14.4 GB	OI, GSM, NGM
1990	Cray Y/MP8 VII	1	**2,600**	512	2 GB	NGM, ETA
1994	Cray C90/16256 [1]	16	**15,300**	2,000	200 GB	NGM, ETA, RUC
1999	IBM RS/6000 SP	768	**700,000**	192,000	4.6 TB	ETA, RUC2, etc
2000	IBM RS/6000 SP	2048	**2,500,000**	256,000	7.5 TB	ETA, RUC2, etc
2003	IBM pSeries 690 [2]	44	**7,300,000**	1,408,000	42 TB	ETA, RUC2, etc

HOME COMPUTER COMPARISION

Year	Model	Processors	Operational Speed (Mflops)	Memory (MB)	Disk storage	Operational Model
1981	Commodore 64	1	**0.16**	0.064	144 KB	—
2003	Pentium 4 2.2 GHz	1	**800**	512	60 GB	Desktop ETA

[1] Caught fire 27 Sep 1999 and was destroyed. Models ran on backup Cray C5 until replaced by IBM RS/6000 SP on 18 Nov 1999.

[2] Became operational 6 June 2003 and is housed at an IBM facility in Gaithersburg, Maryland. Slated for processing upgrades through the year 2009. Ranked as the world's 26th fastest supercomputer in June 2003 according to the industry source Top500.org, but is surpassed by the ECMWF's numerical weather prediction facility which ranks 15th.

Some information obtained from "Maturity of Operational Numerical Weather Prediction: Medium Range", 1998, by Eugenia Kalnay, Stephen J. Lord, and Ronald D. McPherson, Bulletin of the American Meteorological Society.

the right product, such sites are not included in this book as they are often incomplete, outdated, or abandoned. One exception is <www.westwind.ch> which has a surprisingly extensive set of links to international model runs not covered in this book.

■ **Government agencies.** Common sense says that getting it from the horse's mouth is the best thing. Quite often, however, the products placed online at various weather agencies for public consumption are not as pleasing, detailed, or functional as those on other sources.

■ **Universities and institutions.** Academic sources are often eager to demonstrate that they are on the cutting edge, and there you can find some of the best products available anywhere. The College of DuPage <weather.cod.edu> and UCAR <www.rap.ucar.edu> are well-known examples of sites containing excellent product lines. On the other hand there are more than a few universities with excellent meteorology programs but with a neglected or non-existent weather server.

■ **Commercial sources.** For those willing to pay a reasonable fee, a handful of companies generate products in-house from original model output. One of those is Wright Weather <www.wright-weather.com>, which offers some unusual guidance for the United States such as the Japanese JMA/GSM and UKMET model.

The vast majority of Internet weather graphics are generated using GEMPAK, Unisys WXP, or GRADS software. Because of this, it's quite common to notice a familiar look that seems to be shared between two very different sites. For example, NIU <weather.admin.niu.edu> and Unisys <weather.unisys.com> have products with a similar look since they both use the Unisys WXP processor. Government weather sites tend to have complex display software developed inhouse or on contract, and may have very unique and surprising appearances, for better or worse.

Other global models

Finally it should be mentioned that this is not the complete inventory of global models which are available. Dozens of nations have operational global models, including Germany, Russia, China, and India. However they are generally not included in this book either because of translation barriers or because the host agency will not share their graphics publically. As more international NWP products are made available they may be included in future editions of this book.

Right: 3-dimensional displays of meteorological fields are sometimes encountered, but the technique is rarely used among operational meteorologists. Geographical characteristics are disorienting, data is often obscured, and it is difficult for the brain to assimilate the information. How ironic that some television weathercasts insist on "3-D flybys", but when asked to show jet stream charts or isobars they lament that it would confuse their viewers!

an excerpt from
Weather Prediction by Numerical Process

L. F. Richardson, 1922

It took me the best part of six weeks to draw up the computing forms and to work out the new distribution in two vertical columns for the first time. My office was a heap of hay in a cold rest billet. With practice the work of an average computer might go perhaps ten times faster. If the time-step were 3 hours, then 32 individuals could just compute two points so as to keep pace with the weather, if we allow nothing for the very great gain in speed which is invariably noticed when a complicated operation is divided up into simpler parts, upon which individuals specialize. If the co-ordinate chequer were 200 km square in plan, there would be 3200 columns on the complete map of the globe. In the tropics the weather is often foreknown, so that we may say 2000 active columns. So that 32 x 2000 = 64,000 computers would be needed to race the weather for the whole globe. That is a staggering figure. Perhaps in some years' time it may be possible to report a simplification of the process. But in any case, the organization indicated is a central forecast-factory for the whole globe, or for portions extending to boundaries where the weather is steady, with individual computers specializing on the separate equations. Let us hope for their sakes that they are moved on from time to time to new operations.

After so much hard reasoning, may one play with a fantasy? Imagine a large hall like a theatre, except that the circles and galleries go right round through the space usually occupied by the stage. The walls of this chamber are painted to form a map of the globe. The ceiling represents the north polar regions, England is in the gallery, the tropics in the upper circle, Australia on the dress circle and the antarctic in the pit. A myriad computers are at work upon the weather of the part of the map where each sits, but each computer attends only to one equation or part of an equation. The work of each region is coordinated by an official of higher rank. Numerous little "night signs" display the instantaneous values so that neighbouring computers can read them. Each number is thus displayed in three adjacent zones so as to maintain communication to the North and South on the map. From the floor of the pit a tall pillar rises to half the height of the hall. It carries a large pulpit on its top. In this sits the man in charge of the whole theatre; he is surrounded by several assistants and messengers. One of his duties is to maintain a uniform speed of progress in all parts of the globe. In this respect he is like the conductor of an orchestra in which the instruments are slide-rules and calculating machines. But instead of waving a baton he turns a beam of rosy light upon any region that is running ahead of the rest, and a beam of blue light upon those who are behindhand.

Four senior clerks in the central pulpit are collecting the future weather as fast as it is being computed, and despatching it by pneumatic carrier to a quiet room. There it will be coded and telephoned to the radio transmitting station.

Messengers carry piles of used computing forms down to a storehouse in the cellar.

In a neighbouring building there is a research department, where they invent improvements. But these is much experimenting on a small scale before any change is made in the complex routine of the computing theatre. In a basement an enthusiast is observing eddies in the liquid lining of a huge spinning bowl, but so far the arithmetic proves the better way. In another building are all the usual financial, correspondence and administrative offices. Outside are playing fields, houses, mountains and lakes, for it was thought that those who compute the weather should breathe of it freely.

Ensemble Predictions

Ensemble predictions are collections of two or more numerical weather prediction solutions, valid for the same location and forecast time. Combined with each other, each solution, called a *member*, gives a range of possible outcomes.

Given a set of starting conditions, a forecast model will always come to the exact same conclusion, even if it is run a century into the future. However to have a range of outcomes, it is necessary to introduce variability into the model. How can this be done?

The answer is to assume there are slight errors in the starting analysis, and make subtle adjustments before generating each forecast run. This is called a *perturbation* for initial conditions (sometimes abbreviated "IC"). However, another approach is to assume that the model's approximations in its equations or algorithms are a greater cause of errors. In this case, the analysis field is held constant and the model is run multiple times with different physics, dynamics, and parameterizations. This is known as a perturbation for the model's physics. In many cases ensembles are created with a blend of each type of perturbation.

Surprisingly, ensemble forecasting has been done for well over 35 years, in the tried-and-true method where forecasters compare the LFM to the NGM, the RUC to the Eta, and the Spectral to the ECMWF run. This is sometimes referred to as the "poor man's ensemble". However, many experienced forecasters still believe there is enormous value in comparing different models, and have expressed a desire for different model types and their ensembles to be included as part of an ensemble package.

Ensembles can be displayed in a number of different ways:

Ensemble mean. This chart is a mathematical average of all available model solutions for a given point in time. The results tend to look excessively smoothed, however the consensus on weather feature locations are immediately apparent.

Spaghetti diagram. This type of diagram shows one or two selected isopleths from each model combined together on one map. The isopleths look like long noodles of spaghetti overlapping one another, thus the name "spaghetti diagram". As a general rule, the more spread out the isopleths are, the weaker the confidence in the forecast for that area.

Standard deviation. A measure of the difference in all of the fields can be computed to show standard deviation. Where values are higher, there is less confidence in that area.

Great sites with real-time data for this product . . .
○ CPC — **www.cpc.ncep.noaa.gov/products/predictions**
○ EMC — **wwwt.emc.ncep.noaa.gov/mmb/SREF/SREF.html**
○ Canada CMC — **weatheroffice.ec.gc.ca/ensemble**

■ The ensemble approach is valuable because a single high-resolution numerical model forecast represents only one of an infinite number of possible solutions. The ensemble approach attempts to provide the forecaster with as many different solutions as possible.

■ Much of ensemble forecasting is rooted in the work of MIT meteorologist Edward Lorenz's study of deterministic chaos. It recognizes that the atmosphere is a nonlinear system that cannot be solved by any single deterministic model.

■ Ensemble diagrams are not necessarily applicable to medium and long range forecasts only. They have shown great value in short-term forecasts, where they are called short-range ensemble forecasts (SREF).

■ Ensembles may alert forecasters to patterns shown by only a few ensemble members which might have great significance.

■ As models are being reconfigured at an increasingly rapid pace, making it difficult to establish sets of subjective biases for each model, ensembles have taken an increasingly important role in weather forecasting.

■ Europe's ECMWF model is run 51 times daily from slightly different initial conditions and using different model formulations.

■ Though ensemble forecasting provides an excellent tool for forecasting, it is common for the current weather diagnosis to be neglected. This diagnosis often has a bearing on the ensemble forecast.

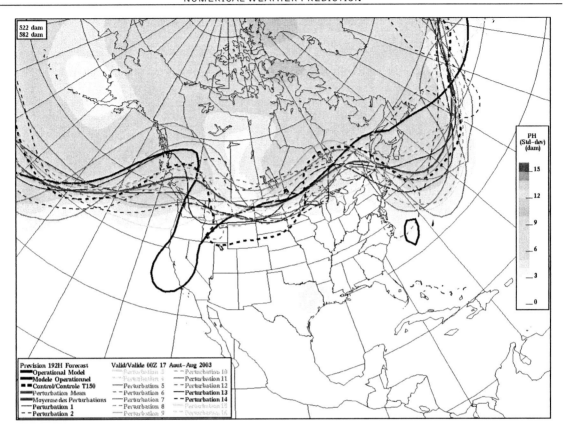

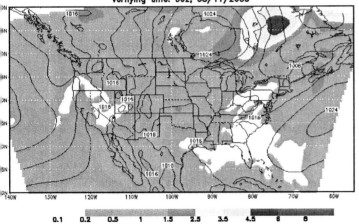

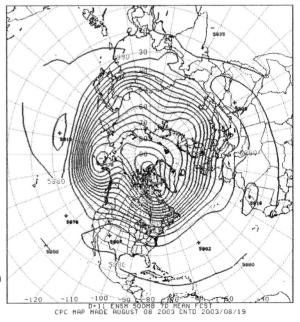

Top: Spaghetti ensemble from CMC GEM runs. *(CMC)*

Above: An Eta mean and standard deviation ensemble. *(NCEP)*

Right: NCEP mean ensemble of 500 mb heights. *(NCEP)*

Model Forecast Soundings

Since models compute expected weather parameters at a large number of vertical points in the atmosphere, it is logical that a thermodynamic diagram of the data can be constructed. This was no easy task in the 1980s, even for National Weather Service field offices, and even in the early 1990s it was difficult to construct model forecast soundings without using the FDUS winds aloft products which were designed for pilots. However, nowadays the rapid advances in computing technology have made model output in sounding format a rather easy task.

There are a multitude of possible uses of model forecast soundings. For example, the sounding depiction format allows cold and warm layers to be properly evaluated, giving a detailed picture of winter precipitation type. In severe weather situations, the depth and relative strength of the elevated mixed layer (EML, the cap) is apparent. Heights of inversions, instability and shear parameters, and much more can easily be determined.

Model forecast soundings, however, are only as good as the model that produces them. A model with poor vertical resolution will produce poor vertical detail. Even the Eta has only 50 mb resolution, which provides conditions only about every 1500 ft (500 m) in the low levels. This can produce soundings that look excessively "smoothed" in convective weather situations and can smear out important, shallow layers.

Furthermore, models do have difficulty with accurately forecasting the boundary layer due to the complex radiative, evaporative, and turbulent processes that occur there. These shortfalls are embodied in model forecast soundings.

Many National Weather Service offices have taken the initiative to identify and publish local studies relating model forecast sounding accuracy to actual soundings, in an attempt to benchmark the model sounding performance. The results are fairly promising but mixed. For example, one study (Evinson and Strobin, 1998) showed that the Eta forecast soundings were too moist in the low-levels, which caused overestimates of the instability in the Great Basin region of the United States.

Forecasters who rely on forecast soundings must be aware of their shortfalls, and must be alert to situations where the model, and in turn the sounding, is likely to fail.

■ Model forecast soundings are an extraction of temperature and dewpoint data in a vertical column above a given point, within a given model run.

■ Model forecast soundings can be extracted from any numerical weather prediction model: Eta, GFS, ECMWF, MM5, and so forth. The only limitation is in the display software used to view the output, and the availability of the raw gridded data.

■ In a convective situation, the vertical resolution of a model forecast sounding is not sufficient to make precise forecasts about cap strength. Many models also have difficulty achieving this level of accuracy, where the difference of half a degree at 700 mb can make or break a severe weather event.

■ These soundings are highly sensitive to conversions from native grid resolution to degraded horizontal or vertical grids, such as when a field is remapped to 40 km or 80 km resolution. The interpolations, particularly across strong gradients, may produce soundings that are not useful. This has been identified as a problem even on NWS AWIPS systems.

■ The model forecast sounding is most prone to errors in the boundary layer, where there are a greater number of factors that can affect the sounding. These include radiation processes, topographical and vegetation effects.

Great sites with real-time data for this product . . .
❍ NIU — **www.stormchaser.niu.edu/machine/fcstsound.html**
❍ COD — **weather.cod.edu/fsound**
❍ NOAA/ARL — **www.arl.noaa.gov/ready/cmet.html**
❍ NCEP/MMB — **www.emc.ncep.noaa.gov/mmb/etasoundings/snding.html**
❍ NOAA/FSL — **www-frd.fsl.noaa.gov/mab/soundings/java/**
❍ Wright-Weather ($) — **www.wright-weather.com**

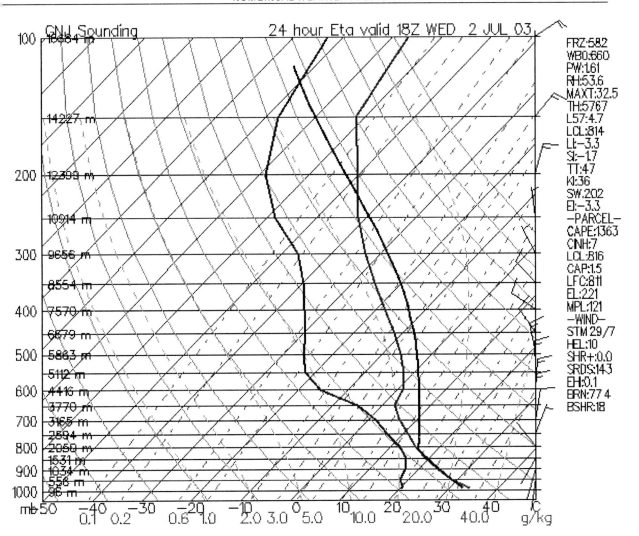

Above: Eta forecast sounding. Note how the temperature and dewpoint traces appear excessively smoothed, which is an artifact of the limited vertical resolution available in numerical models and the relative homogeneity that typically exists in model air masses. *(NCEP)*

Eta Model

The Eta model formed the backbone of most operational forecasting in the United States beginning in the mid-1990s. It is named after the greek letter "eta" and is pronounced EH-ta (not ee-tee-eh). The model was developed in 1978 at the University of Belgrade in Yugoslavia by Zavisa Janjic and Fedor Mesinger, using sigma surfaces to help negotiate the rough terrain in their home country. Janjic brought the model to NMC in the mid-1980s, and its success led to its official implementation in June 1993.

The model was initially run at 00Z and 12Z with a resolution of 80 km at 38 layers. Output fields were generated out to 48 hours. The resolution was boosted to 48 km on 12 October 1995 with major physics improvements.

The NCEP model resolution is 12 km. From this solution, output fields on grids measuring 20, 40, and 80 km in resolution are generated. Thus the term "80 km Eta run" may apply to an output grid but does not correctly describe the model as it is currently run today. In other words, you are receiving the full benefit of the 12 km prediction scheme, but are only looking at the output on a coarser grid.

MODEL BIASES

❏ The Eta model has proven to be an outstanding model. It is more accurate than the NGM, and less prone to convective feedback ("model blowup") compared to the GFS and older NGM. However it comes with a few biases that have been documented.

❏ During the 1990s, the Eta carried a well-known bias during the late spring where it dried out the air mass during the day on the eastern Great Plains, shunting the dryline too far east. Starting around 1998 the Norman OK weather office noticed a moist bias, a reversal of the old problem.

❏ The Eta was observed in 2003 to have frequent problems with spurious cyclones along the Carolinas coast in cold northeasterly flow.

❏ Since about 2000 the Eta has shown a tendency to flip-flip on solutions beyond the 48-hour period. A prudent approach is to rely on the GFS for medium-range periods.

❏ The Eta model, because of its use of eta coordinates, may not have enough vertical resolution over elevated terrain to process the boundary layer conditions correctly.

Great sites with real-time data for this product . . .
○ College of DuPage — **weather.cod.edu/forecast**
○ Unisys — **weather.unisys.com/eta**

■ The ETA model is a finite difference (gridpoint) model that features 12 km resolution. It uses 60 pure eta levels, which are nearly horizontal but mathematically do not intersect the ground.

■ In a series of experiments in the 1990's, when the Eta model was test-run with sigma coordinates, currently used by the NGM and GFS models, it produced an erroneous poleward bias to frontal systems emerging from the Rockies, too-slow polar outbreaks, and cutoff lows too far east in the southwest U.S. These problems are all inherent in the NGM model.

■ Eta-coordinate models are predisposed to underestimating boundary-layer winds in high terrain, and may miss katabatic windstorm situations.

■ CAPE values in the NCEP Eta model are found by lifting the parcel with the highest theta-e in the lowest 70 mb of the atmosphere.

■ Run codes are gf089 (early Eta) and gf085 (Meso/off-time Eta). Output grids are 211/Q (80 km grid), 212/R (40 km grid), and 215/U (20 km grid)

■ **Model milestones**

STANDARD ETA

Date	Type	Wave	Res	Lyrs
1993	Grid	—	80 km	38
1995	Grid	—	48 km	38
1998	Grid	—	32 km	45
2000	Grid	—	22 km	50
2001	Grid	—	12 km	60

MESO-ETA

Date	Type	Wave	Res	Lyrs
1995	Grid	—	29 km	50
1998	Meso-Eta discontinued			

Surface (10m) Wind Speed (knots) / MSLP (mb)

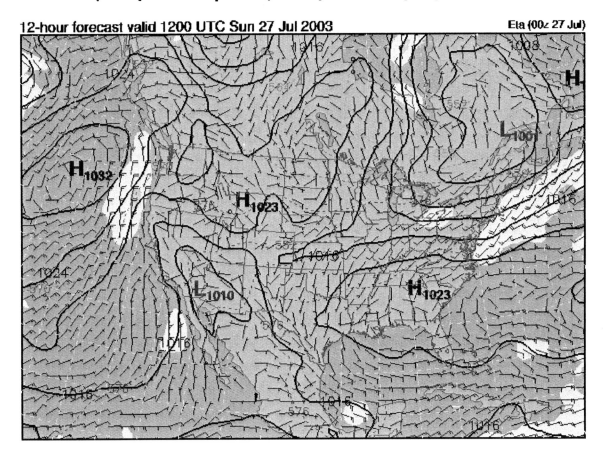

12-hour forecast valid 1200 UTC Sun 27 Jul 2003   Eta (00z 27 Jul)

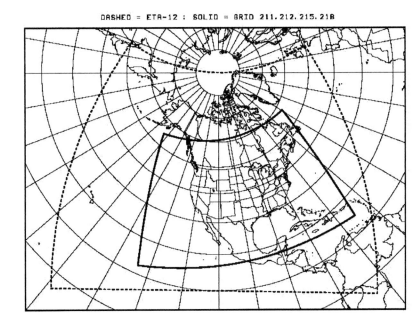

DASHED = ETA-12 ; SOLID = GRID 211.212.215.218

Above: Surface chart as generated from the Eta model and displayed by UCAR. *(UCAR)*

Right: Domain of the Eta model (wide box). The output grid is the smaller solid box. *(NCEP)*

NGM Model
NCEP / Also known as: RAFS

The NGM (Nested Grid Model) was developed as the "next generation" improvement to the old LFM (Limited-area Fine Mesh model) that predominated United States forecasting in the 1970's. It was developed by Norman A. Phillips in 1978.

Operational use of the NGM commenced on 27 March 1985 on the new Cyber 205 supercomputer. An improved physics package was added in August 1986, followed by a fine-mesh grid expansion in February 1987. The model was scaled down to two grids in August 1991, and that concluded work on it with the bigger and better Eta expected to come online. The model was scheduled to be axed by 1998, however it still remained a part of the NCEP model suite as of this writing.

As implied by its name, the NGM uses multiple nested grids: a larger, coarse one to "see" distant systems in Asia, Europe, and elsewhere, and a smaller, denser one focused on North America in which to make highly detailed computations. It is a concept embraced by the Canadian GEM Regional and UKMET models. The NGM was part of a suite called the RAFS (Regional Analysis and Forecasting System), and is still sometimes referred to by that name.

MODEL BIASES

The NGM's dynamics have not been changed since 1990, and as a result a vast storehouse of NGM characteristics, both formal and anecdotal, have accumulated over the years. The most important biases are:

☐ The skill of the NGM is best in the warm season when the atmosphere is less baroclinic.

☐ Surface lows and highs are often too strong over land and too weak over the ocean. This is particularly true in the High Plains of North America.

☐ The model has a poleward bias; in other words, United States systems often appear further north than they should. Systems emerging from the Rocky Mountains are often too far north and too intense.

☐ Digging upper-level troughs show too weak of an amplitude.

☐ Plunging cold outbreaks are moved too slowly.

☐ The NGM forecasts spurious precipitation in the wake of squall lines in the southern Plains, and overdoes precipitation in upslope situations on the Great Plains and along sea breeze convergence zones. However it underforecasts heavy rain events along the Gulf of Mexico coast.

Great sites with real-time data for this product . . .
○ College of DuPage — **weather.cod.edu/forecast**
○ Unisys — **weather.unisys.com/ngm**

■ The NGM is a finite difference (gridpoint) model with a resolution of 84 km. It uses 16 pure sigma (terrain-following) surfaces. The NGM forecasts out to 48 hours.

■ The NGM, being a sigma model, does not handle weather events in the lee of a mountain range very well. Cold air damming and lee-side cyclogenesis may pose significant forecasting problems. Forecasts of cold air damming became much more accurate in 1993 when the Eta came online, providing an alternative to the NGM.

■ Some products, such as instability, use four-layer calculations. The lowest four layers in the NGM span 150 mb of depth, or about 1.5 km (4900 ft).

■ This model uses the nested grid, which combines the advantages of a global model's diminished boundary layer problems with the detailed resolution of a regional model.

■ The NGM's dynamics have not changed since 1990. Therefore its biases are well-documented.

■ The model is a heavy producer of model output statistics (MOS), many of which have been worked up over a period of two decades and account for NGM biases. This is one reason why the NGM has been changed very little and the fact that there is resistance to retiring the NGM.

■ **Model milestones**

Date	Type	Wave	Res	Lyrs
1985	Nest Grid	—	84 km	16

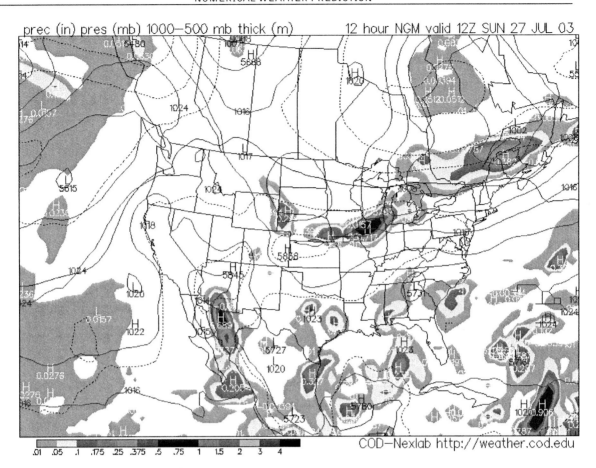

Top: NGM forecast predicting rain along a cold front extending from Chicago to far northern Kansas. *(Unisys)*

Right: Domain of the current two-grid NGM, showing the large 336 km resolution outer grid (large box) and the smaller 84 km grid truncated to fit the Eta analysis grid (small, dark box). This configuration took effect in 1999. *(NCEP)*

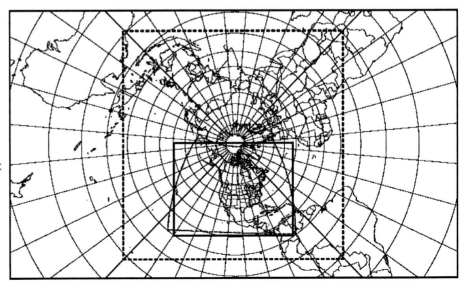

RUC Model

During the late 1980s, ACARS aircraft observations, wind profiler data, and an increasingly dense surface network were all rapidly coming online. It became quite obvious that a new model was needed to synthesize all of this mesoscale data at rapid frequency. There was also a need for a model that would end the long waits for major model runs to finish while weather was changing by the hour. Thus, the RUC (Rapid Update Cycle) model was born.

The model was initially developed by the NOAA Forecast Systems Laboratory, where it was known as MAPS (Mesoscale Analysis and Prediction System). It underwent about three years of testing, and finally the completed model was implemented at the National Meteorological Center (NMC, now NCEP) in September 1994.

In April 1998 the RUC-2 model was introduced, replacing the original RUC. It added considerable improvements to the physics, parameterizations, and model resolution. GOES precipitable water data was introduced with this upgrade.

On 17 April 2002, the RUC20 model was introduced, replacing the RUC2. It doubled the resolution and added 10 new vertical layers. There were also vast improvements to integration of surface data, improved diagnostic routines, better cloud parameterization, and inputs every 6 hours from the Eta run. Analysis was done through old-fashioned optimum interpolation (OI) up until sometime in 2003 when the 3DVAR method was integrated.

MODEL BIASES

Although biases in the RUC and RUC-2 have been documented, none have been forthcoming for the RUC20.

However the sigma-theta coordinate system delivers several advantages for the RUC model. First and foremost, it is theoretically much better at forecasting the onset of isentropic upglide compared to eta and pure sigma coordinate systems, however the RUC is theoretically worse than the Eta run at handling mountain interactions such as cold air damming and lee cyclogenesis. The coordinate system also allows for better modelling of surface heating and dynamical mixing, as well as excellent physical representation of processes such as snow cover and evaporation.

Great sites with real-time data for this product . . .
- College of DuPage — **weather.cod.edu/forecast**
- Unisys — **weather.unisys.com/ruc**
- Ohio State — **twister.sbs.ohio-state.edu/models/ruc**
- NOAA/ARL — **www.arl.noaa.gov/ready/rucanim.html**
- UCAR — **www.rap.ucar.edu/weather/model**
- NCEP (official RUC site) — **maps.fsl.noaa.gov**

■ The RUC is a finite difference (gridpoint) model with 20-km resolution. It uses 50 hybrid sigma-theta levels, consisting of terrain-following sigma surfaces close to the surface and isentropic (theta, or potential temperature) surfaces from the middle troposphere upward.

■ The RUC II or RUC-2 refers to an older model that was discontinued in 2002. The current RUC has a gridpoint resolution of 301 x 225, compared with 151 x 113 in RUC-2.

■ The RUC model's use of a sigma-theta hybrid allows it to achieve excellent resolution in baroclinic zones, such as along fronts.

■ One of the main drives in the creation of the RUC20 model was to implement better quantitative precipitation forecasts. This was done through a sophisticated cloud microphysics algorithm and better convective parameterization.

■ Boundary conditions for the RUC come from the ETA model. This allows the RUC to "see" systems approaching its grid edges.

■ **Model milestones**

ORIGINAL RUC (RUC1)

Date	Type	Wave	Res	Lyrs
1994	Grid	—	60 km	25
1998	Discontinued			

RUC-2 (RUC40)

Date	Type	Wave	Res	Lyrs
1998	Grid	—	40 km	40
2002	Discontinued			

RUC20

Date	Type	Wave	Res	Lyrs
2002	Grid	—	20 km	50

Wind Speed (knots) / MSLP (mb)

06 Hour forecast valid 1200 UTC Sun 27 Jul 2003   RUC (06z 27 Jul)

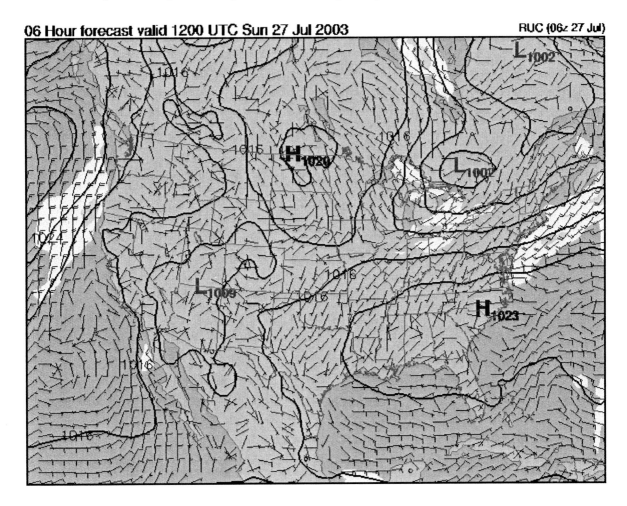

Top: RUC-20 model prediction. Plots with wind barbs, such as these from the UCAR weather site <www.rap.ucar.edu> are extremely useful for helping pin down frontal locations. *(UCAR)*

Right: The detailed terrain field present in the RUC-20 model. The chart coverage corresponds to the actual geographic coverage of the model. The RUC's sigma surfaces "bend" over these terrain features. *(NCEP)*

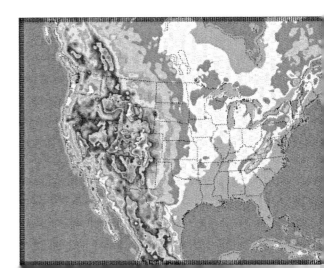

GFS Model

AVN, MRF

The term GFS (Global Forecast System) is the United State's global forecasting model and the counterpart to the European ECMWF model. It encompasses a broad suite of products that includes the AVN (Aviation Model), the GDAS (Global Data Assimilation System), and the discontinued MRF (Medium Range Forecast) model.

The model was first introduced operationally as the GSM (Global Spectral Model) on 18 March 1981, replacing the PE (Primitive Equation) model that had been operational since 1966. This made it known colloquially as "The Spectral Model" among American forecasters. It was the first operational spectral model, which visualized the atmosphere as mathematical waves rather than arrays of data at gridpoints. It was a 30-wave 12-level model, in other words, weather systems were defined as a series of 30 waves around the hemisphere, and 12 horizontal surfaces were used to represent the depth of the troposphere. The 30 waves gave it an effective resolution of 465 km.

In 1985, the GSM was split into two runs: the AVN (Aviation) for short-range forecasting and the MRF (Medium Range Forecast) model for medium-range forecasting. The models were identical, but the MRF was started several hours later than the AVN to make full use of all available data.

On 23 April 2002, the MRF and AVN were consolidated back into one run, called the GFS.

MODEL BIASES

☐ The GFS has occasional problems with "precipitation bombs": a spurious convective complex with no apparent source. This is most likely to occur on the High Plains of the United States and in the Ohio River Valley during the warm season. However it has been seen in nearly all geographic locations worldwide. For more information see <www.hpc.ncep.noaa.gov/qpfbombs>.
☐ In meridional flow the GFS can be too aggressive with amplifying the pattern and driving cold outbreaks southward, particularly past 72 hours. It is a good idea to consider other guidance such the ECMWF.
☐ In split flow patterns, particularly during the cool season, the GFS has a tendency to phase the waves in each jet into a large long wave. This may overstrengthen surface systems on the High Plains of the United States. The UKMET model has been noted as a better choice in such situations.

Great sites with real-time data for this product . . .
○ NCEP DIFAX — **weather.noaa.gov/fax/nwsfax.html**

■ The GFS is a 254-wave spectral model with triangular truncation. This is a resolution of about 55 km. At the 84-hour point it becomes a 170-wave 42-level model, and at the 180-hour point it becomes a 126-wave 28-level model. The GFS uses 64 pure sigma (terrain-following) levels. Time integration is leapfrog and semi-implicit.

■ Although the GFS is a spectral model, it offloads fields to a 768 x 384 point Gaussian grid for physics and nonlinear calculations.

■ It takes NCEP's IBM supercomputers about 12 minutes of computation time to complete the entire GFS run. However a considerable amount of time is spent preparing the data and the model for execution.

■ The GFS, being a sigma model, is prone to errors in the lee of mountain ranges. It has inherent problems with lee-side weather systems and cold-air damming. However it has excellent resolution near the ground and will accurately handle diurnal heating and low-level winds and moisture.

■ The GFS is run four times a day (00Z, 06Z, 12Z, and 18Z) out to 384 hours.

■ **Model milestones**

Date	Type	Wave	Res	Lyrs
1980	Spectral	R30	442 km	12
1983	Spectral	R40	331 km	12
1985	Spectral	R40	331 km	18
1987	Spectral	T80	166 km	18
1991	Spectral	T126	105 km	18
1993	Spectral	T126	105 km	28
2000	Spectral	T170	78 km	42
2002	Spectral	T254	52 km	64

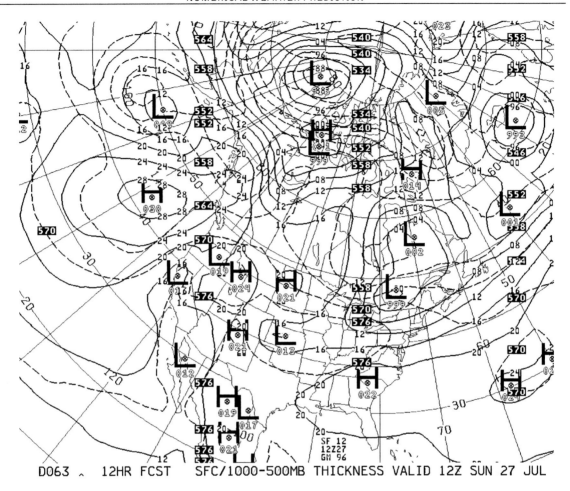

D063 ∧ 12HR FCST   SFC/1000-500MB THICKNESS VALID 12Z SUN 27 JUL

Above: The GFS run as depicted by the legacy NCEP DIFAX chart series. *(NCEP)*

Right: Just because you're not in North America or Europe doesn't mean that you can't get detailed weather charts. Depending on how adventurous your favorite Internet graphics site is, there is no reason that charts such as this GFS view of 500 mb heights and vorticity in India can't be displayed. This example comes from a special Institute of Global Environment and Society site using the GrADS viewer <www.monsoondata.org>. *(IGES)*

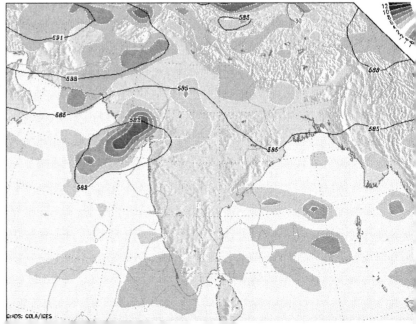

MM5 Model

The MM5 is not the name for a suite of products but rather for a "brand" of model, the Mesoscale Model Fifth Generation developed by the University Corporation for Atmospheric Research (UCAR) in collaboration with Pennsylvania State University (PSU). It was designed to be the ultimate solution to a pressing requirement in the research community: the need for a small-scale model that was not locked onto a large, regional domain.

The model was first developed as early as 1972, and as it came to the forefront of mesoscale meteorology with the arrival of powerful computing technology, the MM5 was released to the weather community in early 1994. The first generation of the model was optimized for Cray systems. The second version, released the same year, supported more operating systems and included improved physics packages.

The primary advantage of the MM5 are two things: its mesoscale coverage and is its portability. Since it is adapted for high-resolution terrain and uses non-hydrostatic calculations, it is perhaps one of the best models available for looking at extremely small-scale processes. It is perfect for examining mesoscale convective systems, fronts, tertiary circulations, and urban meteorology effects. Furthermore its design for portability allows it to be run on a broad range of Unix systems, with vast flexibility on the resolution, the domain size, and other configuration options. The source code is in FORTRAN and can be easily modified to customize the model.

MODEL BIASES

Unfortunately it is impossible to give a description of MM5 model biases since it is run by different users in a variety of configurations and with varying data sources. However the consensus is that the MM5 does an excellent job with mesoscale weather systems, true to its design.

■ The MM5 model is a finite difference (gridpoint) model with pure sigma (terrain-following) surfaces. The horizontal and vertical resolution is set by the user.

■ The model is non-hydrostatic, which means that it can be run at unusually small scales (with resolutions less than 10 km).

■ The MM5, being a sigma model, is prone to errors in the lee of mountain ranges. It will have problems with lee-side weather systems and cold-air damming. However it has excellent resolution near the ground and will accurately handle diurnal heating and low-level winds and moisture.

■ The MM5 is currently in operational use in such exotic locations as Kenya, Mozambique, China, Peru, and Colombia.

■ Is there an MM4? Yes, there is. Papers were published on this preliminary version in 1987 by Hsie and Anthes.

■ Model milestones
February 1994	Initial release
July 1994	Version 2 (V2)
June 1999	Version 3 (V3)

Great sites with real-time data for this product . . .
- ○ UCAR (US) — **rain.mmm.ucar.edu/mm5**
- ○ NASA/GHCC (US) — **www.ghcc.msfc.nasa.gov/Model/model_mm5.html**
- ○ US Air Force (US/worldwide) — **https://afweather.afwa.af.mil/met/na_mod_mm5.html**
- ○ U of Washington (US West Coast) — **www.atmos.washington.edu/mm5rt**
- ○ U of Wiscosin (US) — **aurora.aos.wisc.edu/current.shtml**
- ○ Naval Postgraduate School (US West Coast) — **www.weather.nps.navy.mil/~dkmiller/MM5**
- ○ Tucson NWS (SW US) — **nimbo.wrh.noaa.gov/Tucson/mm5/mm5tus.html**
- ○ SUNY (East US) — **cheget.msrc.sunysb.edu/html/alt_mm5.cgi**
- ○ Mexican weather service (Mexico) — **galileo.imta.mx**
- ○ *Official MM5 page* — **www.mmm.ucar.edu/mm5**

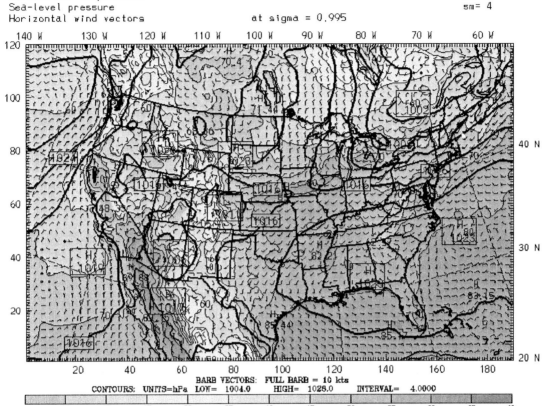

Real-time MM5 Domain 1
Fcst: 12 h
Surface air temperature
Sea-level pressure
Horizontal wind vectors   at sigma = 0.995

Init: 00 UTC Sun 27 Jul 03
Valid: 12 UTC Sun 27 Jul 03 (06 MDT Sun 27 Jul 03)
sm= 1
sm= 4

BARB VECTORS: FULL BARB = 10 kts
CONTOURS: UNITS=hPa   LOW= 1004.0   HIGH= 1028.0   INTERVAL= 4.0000

35   40   45   50   55   60   65   70   75   80   85   °F
Model info: V2.12+ Grell   MRF PBL   Simple Ice   30 km, 27 levels, 90 sec

Above: MM5 prediction for the United States generated by the people that brought it into existence <rain.mmm.ucar.edu>. *(UCAR)*

Right: MM5 output for the Los Angeles area, coastal range, and southern San Joaquin Valley. *(Navy/NPS)*

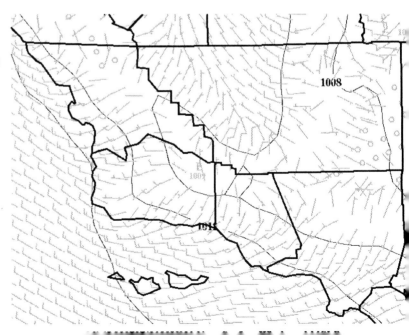

NOGAPS Model

The NOGAPS (Navy Operational Global Atmospheric Prediction System) is a global spectral model that runs twice a day out to 144 hours. It is managed by the U.S. Navy's Fleet Numerical Meteorology Center (FNMOC). The NOGAPS model uses the multivariate version of the OI (optimal interpolation) analysis scheme. It executes on SGI Origin 3000 supercomputers at FNMOC in Monterey, California.

The Navy had been experimenting with numerical models as early as 1959. In the mid-1970s there was a push for a global spectral model to be developed, and the Naval Research Laboratory produced the first version of NOGAPS in 1982. It was a finite-difference (gridpoint) model. Unfortunately during long-term testing it was found that NOGAPS was a poor contender to the AVN/MRF and ECMWF models. NOGAPS was scrapped in 1987 and rebuilt as a spectral model, yielding a much more robust system.

The model was good enough to become operational on January 1988 and has gone through a series of upgrades. The current NOGAPS release, V4.0, was fielded on 18 September 2002.

MODEL BIASES

❏ During later time frames, generally past 2-3 days, mature cyclones over land tend to be too deep, while those over the ocean tend to be too weak. The best skill is with deepening lows over North America, but filling is too slow.
❏ Over the ocean during meridional flow, deepening cyclones are moved too slowly and filling ones are moved too far poleward.
❏ Over the ocean during zonal flow, deepening cyclones are moved too fast and filling ones are moved too far poleward.
❏ Surface and upper-level cyclones equatorward of the polar front jet are deepened too slowly, while those poleward are deepened too rapidly.
❏ Oceanic anticyclones are slightly too intense.
❏ The model does a good job handling transitions from digging troughs into cutoff lows in the spring and fall.
❏ During the cool season, upper-level troughs are dug too aggressively on the U.S. West Coast beyond 84 hours.
❏ The model is slightly overprogressive with upper troughs in zonal flow.
❏ Tropical cyclones tend to be moved too slowly.

Great sites with real-time data for this product . . .
❍ U.S. Navy — **www.fnoc.navy.mil/PUBLIC/WXMAP/ index.html**
❍ Wright Weather ($) — **www.wright-weather.com**

■ The NOGAPS model is a spectral model that uses 239 waves with triangular truncation, achieving 56 km resolution. It uses 9-minute time steps. The model uses 30 hybrid sigma-pressure levels, consisting of sigma (terrain-following) surfaces close to the ground and pressure surfaces above the middle troposphere.

■ As with the GFS model, fields are mapped onto a 0.5 deg Gaussian grid for physics processing.

■ The NOGAPS hybrid vertical coordinate scheme is also used by the ECMWF, UKMET, and JMA models.

■ The skill of the NOGAPS model is generally considered to be slightly less than that of the GFS and ECMWF.

■ NOGAPS is not very sensitive to bombs (extratropical cyclones, particularly off the coast in the winter, which deepen at a very rapid rate). The GFS and ECMWF are better at detecting the unfolding of a bomb.

■ NOGAPS tends to generate spurious tropical cyclones past the 48-hour point.

■ **Model milestones**

Date	Type	Wave	Res	Lyrs
1988	Spectral	T47	282 km	18
1989	Spectral	T79	168 km	18
1994	Spectral	T159	83 km	18
1998	Spectral	T159	83 km	24
2002	Spectral	T239	56 km	30

■ **Operational supercomputers**

1992 — Cray Y/MP C916/8128/ 8
1994 — Cray Y-MP/C916/8256/ 8
1999 — SGI Origin 2000 / 128
2001 — SGI Origin 3000 / 512

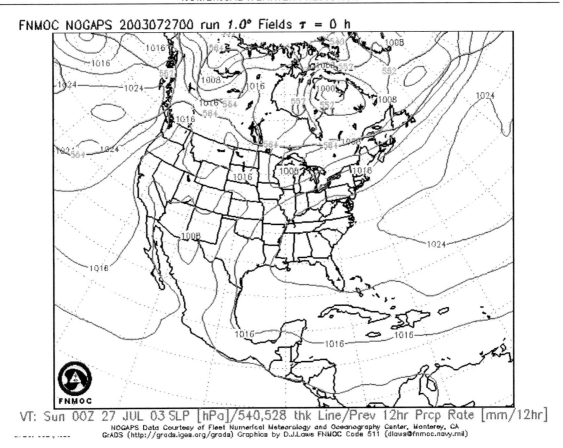

FNMOC NOGAPS 2003072700 run *1.0°* Fields τ = 0 h

VT: Sun 00Z 27 JUL 03 SLP [hPa]/540,528 thk Line/Prev 12hr Prcp Rate [mm/12hr]
NOGAPS Data Courtesy of Fleet Numerical Meteorology and Oceanography Center, Monterey, CA
GrADS (http://grads.iges.org/grads) Graphics by D.J.Laws FNMOC Code 511 (dlaws@fnmoc.navy.mil)

Above: NOGAPS forecast as produced by the U.S. Navy FNMOC web site. *(FNMOC)*

Right: The NOGAPS model has proven to be an excellent worldwide forecasting tool, including for Europe. This depiction is available at <www.wetterzentrale.de>. 500 mb contours are drawn as shading. An occlusion is over Scandinavia, with a potent baroclinic system forming west-southwest of Ireland. *(Wetterzentrale)*

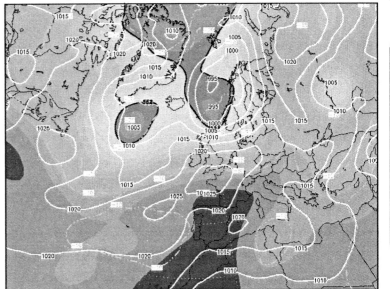

Init : Sun.27JUL2003 12Z   Valid: Sat.02AUG2003 12Z
500 hPa Geopot.(gpdm), T (Grad C) und Bodendruck (hPa)

Daten: 00z/12z-Lauf des NOGAPS-Modells der US-Navy
Wetterzentrale Karlsruhe
Top Karten : http://www.wetterzentrale.de/topkarten/

WRF Model

The Weather Research and Forecasting (WRF) model is currently in development and is expected to become operational by late 2004 or 2005. It is expected to dominate American numerical weather prediction in the latter half of the decade. The WRF is created under a partnership between the National Center for Atmospheric Research (NCAR), the NOAA Forecast Systems Laboratory (FSL), the National Centers for Environmental Prediction (NCEP), and several other institutions. The WRF is expected to become part of the operational forecasting suite at NCEP and many other agencies by 2005, and may ultimately replace NCEP's MM5, RUC, and ETA.

Envisioning the WRF model during the mid-1990s, its creators sought to replicate Europe's success in orchestrating development of a numerical model with great research and operational support, with the idea of creating a new mesoscale model that would be even better than the enormously popular MM5. Development teams had the task of designing and developing an advanced numerical model that would be flexible, portable, and scalable. A prototype was fielded in 2000, and continues to undergo development and tweaking work as of this writing.

The WRF can be considered a community model, composed of algorithms from many different institutions and agencies that can be selected by the user. The source code uses a layered software architecture that encapsulates low-level processing within the model to make custom routines flexible, independent, and efficient. The model runs grids smaller than 10 km, and is capable of these tight resolutions since it is a non-hydrostatic model. The WRF is designed for portability, with the ability to run under a number of architectures including parallel processors.

Other models are typically used to feed it with initial conditions. The most common source is ETA or RUC data, thus it may be referred to as "ETA WRF" or "RUC WRF". It also considers land use, soil texture, and topography as input fields. The model allows for a variety of different algorithms covering turbulence and diffusion, microphysics, radiation, boundary layer, and cumulus processes.

MODEL BIASES

A collection of WRF model biases is not practical due to the wide range of physics and dynamics packages and model configurations that are in use.

Great sites with real-time data for this product . . .
- ❑ ilMeteo (Italy) — **www.ilmeteo.com/wrf.php**
- ❑ NSSL — **www.nssl.noaa.gov/wrf/**
- ❑ UCAR (links) — **box.mmm.ucar.edu/wrf/REAL_TIME/**

■ The WRF is a finite difference (gridpoint) non-hydrostatic model. It may use either eta or zeta vertical coordinate systems. The horizontal and vertical resolution is completely dependent on user specifications, and is often less than 10 km.

■ The model allows unlimited options for dynamics and physics packages, and can be tailored to a substantial degree. This allows the end user to select the ideal configuration for a given purpose.

■ Only research runs are available at this time. The model has not been commissioned for official forecasting.

■ The WRF, taking on dual roles as a mesoscale and regional model, is expected to serve as a replacement for the MM5 and RUC, and should eventually replace the NCEP ETA run.

■ The WRF will support nested grids, which was the concept of the NGM model in the 1980s.

■ The first release of the WRF was on November 30, 2000. Real-time 30-km resolution forecasts began trickling out from NCAR in March 2001.

■ As of mid-2003 the WRF did not allow the ability to ingest surface observations directly.

■ Future upgrades are expected to include input of actual observed data from the MM5 model, output in other formats besides netCDF, new microphysics processes, and more.

■ Full information about the WRF model can be found at <www.wrf-model.org>

Surface 2 m T (F, color) SLP (mb) and winds (kts)

WRF MASS 10KM   2003-08-02 00:00:00 = 2003-08-01 12:00:00 + 12 h

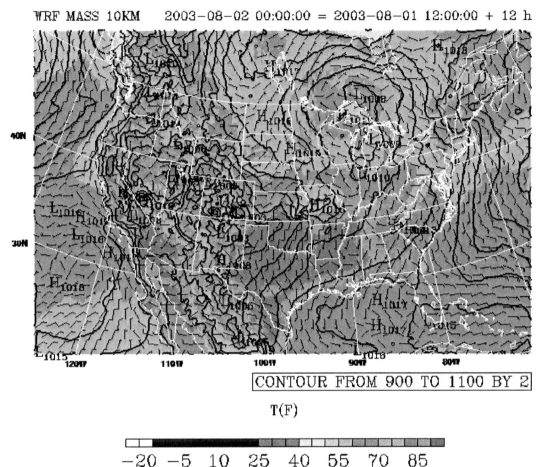

CONTOUR FROM 900 TO 1100 BY 2

T(F)

−20 −5 10 25 40 55 70 85

Above: WRF forecast as obtained from UCAR. *(UCAR)*

Right: Experimental WRF output generated at the National Severe Storms Laboratory. *(NSSL)*

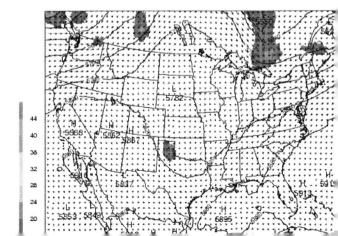

500 Z WND VORT

VALID 12Z 14 JUN 03

WRF DX 12 km
00-H   FCST
12.0 KM LMB CON GRD

ECMWF Model (Europe)

The ECMWF is the name for a meteorological center as well as a model: The European Centre for Medium-Range Weather Forecasts. The center was envisioned in 1967 as part of a resolution to develop a multinational weather center, and opened its doors in 1973.

The first operational ECMWF model forecast was produced on 1 August 1979 using a Cray 1A supercomputer. It was a 15-level gridpoint model with a resolution of 200 km. In April 1983, ECMWF adopted a spectral model with 63 waves and 16 layers. In 1992 an ensemble forecasting system was added. In April 1995 parameterization of clouds was added. In 1996 the Optimum Interpolation analysis scheme was replaced by the 3DVAR method. The WAM ocean wave model was introduced in 1992, followed by integration with the atmospheric model in 1998.

Currently, the ECMWF model is run on an IBM Cluster 1600 system, featuring a scalar rather than vector architecture. It consists of 30 p690 servers. This new computer system produced its first ECMWF forecast in March 2003.

MODEL BIASES

☐ The ECMWF is considered to be superior at forecasting upper-level heights during the cold season, particularly with respect to wave number transitions and the onset of +PNA circulation episodes (west Canada ridge with polar air affecting the central and eastern U.S.).
☐ Excellent at handling timing of shallow cold air outbreaks, particularly in the Great Plains.
☐ Notorious for overdeveloping or overpopulating cutoff lows, particularly in the southwestern U.S. However this yields somewhat better skill than other models in spring when cutoff lows are most common. The model is also too slow or even retrogressive with cutoff lows, which are sometimes even erroneously shunted westward underneath the Pacific subtropical high.
☐ Has a high height bias in the upper troposphere, and this produces a high thickness bias.
☐ Has a meridional bias, making upper air patterns unusually amplified and surface systems more intense and more slow. Therefore a progressive pattern forecast by the ECMWF is significant and probably meaningful.

Great sites with real-time data for this product . . .
❍ College of DuPage — **weather.cod.edu/forecast**
❍ Wetterzentrale (Europe) — **www.wetterzentrale.de/topkarten**
❍ ECMWF Data Server — **www.ecmwf.int**
❍ Unisys — **weather.unisys.com/ecmwf**

■ The ECMWF model is a 511-wave spectral model with triangular truncation. It uses 60 hybrid sigma-pressure levels, consisting of sigma (terrain-following) surfaces near the ground and pressure surfaces aloft.

■ The ECMWF model is usually the most reliable source of numerical forecast output for any random area on the planet.

■ A considerable amount of data is restricted from the public, in particular model fields before the 72 hour point. This has been a longtime issue of debate between European users and institutional concerns. Even European hobbyists must turn to the NOGAPS, GFS, and UKMET to examine detailed products and earlier time periods.

■ Model milestones

Date Lyrs	Type	Wave	Res	
1979	Grid	—	200 km	15
1983	Spectral	T63	211 km	16
1985	Spectral	T106	125 km	16
1986	Spectral	T106	125 km	19
1991	Spectral	T213	62 km	31
1998	Spectral	T319	42 km	50
1999	Spectral	T319	42 km	60
2000	Spectral	T511	26 km	60

■ Supercomputers

1976 — CDC 6600
1978 — Cray 1A
1984 — Cray X/MP 22
1986 — Cray Y/MP 8/8 64
1992 — Cray Y-MP/C916/16128/ 16
1994 — Cray Y/MP C916/16256/ 16
1994 — Cray T3D MCA128-8/ 128
1996 — Fujitsu VPP700/46/ 46
1997 — Fujitsu VPP/700/116/ 116
2000 — Fujitsu VPP5000/100/ 100
2003 — IBM pSeries 690 Turbo / 960

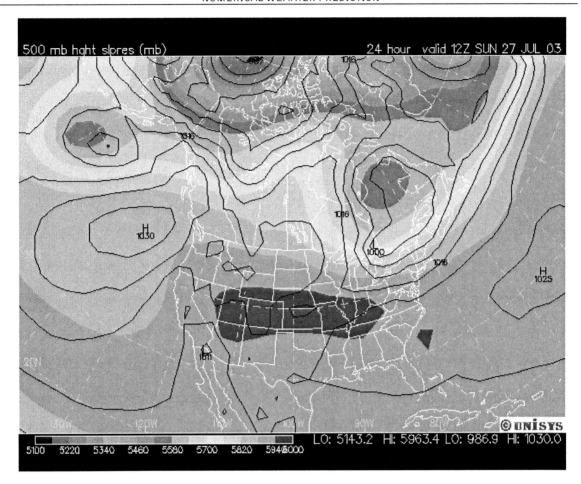

Above: ECMWF output as provided on the Unisys site <weather.unisys.com>. *(Unisys)*

Right: The ECMWF supercomputer facility near Reading, England consists of two sets of 30 IBM pSeries 690 processors driven by the AIX-L operating system. It was installed in late 2002 and operational in 2003. A recent industry ranking classified it as the 15th most powerful system in the world. Each cluster contains 1.35 terabytes of memory and 4.2 terabytes of disk storage. In a single second it can make calculations that would take 17 million years for a person to do by hand. *(ECMWF)*

UKMET Model (U.K.)

UNIFIED MODEL SYSTEM

The term UKMET is a shorthand phrase describing the Unified Model System, a sophisticated model operated by the Met Office, the British government weather service. The system has been run for decades at the Bracknell facility west of London, but during the summer of 2003 the facility was being moved to the Met Office's new headquarters at Exeter in Devon.

Great Britain's expertise with numerical models goes back to 1959, when the University of Manchester successfully ran a numerical prediction on a Ferranti Mark 1 computer. Almost immediately the British Met Office put a Ferranti Mercury computer to work, producing experimental 36-hour forecasts for the eastern Atlantic and western Europe. It took about 6 hours to produce each complete forecast.

With a new computer purchase in 1965, the Met Office introduced its first operational model that covered 30 hours and up to 72 hours experimentally. This was improved further with an IBM 360 acquisition in 1972 and introduction of a nested grid scheme. The model has undergone upgrades since then, the latest being the addition of a new physics package nick-named "New Dynamics" on 7 August 2002. The model is scheduled to be moved to new NEC SX-6 systems in March 2004.

MODEL BIASES

Many biases published for the UKMET model are probably obsolete due to the thoroughly retooled physics package that was introduced in August 2002. Very little information on the new model characteristics are available at this time. However the following biases are traditionally associated with the UKMET, and should be watched for in case they have carried over into the new implementation:

☐ A persistent warm bias in the middle troposphere
☐ Problems with shallow cold air outbreaks
☐ A zonal bias; i.e. a refusal to amplify long wave troughs
☐ An equatorward bias for surface and upper-air systems.
☐ An equatorward bias for the polar jet and prevailing wester-lies
☐ Short waves moved too fast

■ The Met Office Unified Model System ("UKMET") is a finite difference (gridpoint) model which uses nested grids and spherical coordinates. The global model features 60 km resolution with 30 hybrid levels. The mesoscale model features 10 to 15 km resolution with 38 hybrid levels.

■ The hybrid levels are sigma-pressure levels, with sigma (terrain-following) coordinates close to the ground and pressure surfaces aloft.

■ The UKMET hybrid vertical coordinate scheme is also used by the ECMWF, NOGAPS, and JMA models.

■ The global model has 62 km resolution (432x325 points), while the nested mesoscale model has a resolution of 17 km (146x182 points).

■ **Model milestones**

Date	Type	Wave	Res	Lyrs
1959	Grid	—	320 km	2
1965	Grid	—	300 km	3
1972	Nest Grid	—	100 km	10
1982	Nest Grid	—	75 km	15
1991	Nest Grid	—	17 km	19

■ **Operational supercomputers**

1959 — Ferranti Mercury
1965 — English Electric KDF 9
1972 — IBM 360/95
1982 — CDC Cyber 205
1991 — Cray Y-MP8/864/ 8
1994 — Cray Y-MP C916/16256/ 16
1996 — Cray T3E/ 128
1997 — Cray T3E900/ 876
2004 — NEC SX-6 (planned)

Great sites with real-time data for this product . . .
○ Ohio State (US) — **twister.sbs.ohio-state.edu/models/ukmet**
○ Iowa State (US) — **cumulus.geol.iastate.edu/ukmet.html**
○ *UK NCAS (technical)* — **www.cgam.nerc.ac.uk/um/doc/umug**
○ *UK Met Office (official)* — **www.meto.govt.uk/research/nwp/numerical/operational**

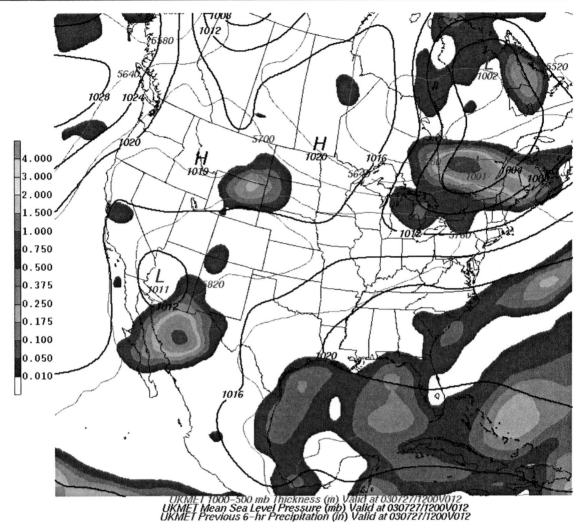

UKMET 1000–500 mb Thickness (m) Valid at 030727/1200V012
UKMET Mean Sea Level Pressure (mb) Valid at 030727/1200V012
UKMET Previous 6–hr Precipitation (in) Valid at 030727/1200V012

Above: The Ohio State University server provides perhaps the largest, most useful UKMET maps of North America on the Internet. *(OSU)*

Right: The nested mesoscale subset of the Unified Model System covers Great Britain and part of northwest Europe at 17 km resolution. The remainder of the globe is covered at 62 km resolution. *(Tim Vasquez)*

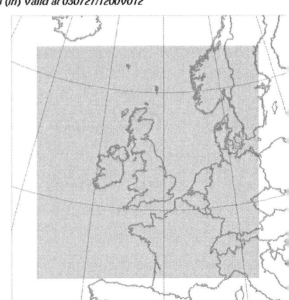

GEM Model (Canada)
RFE, EFR, SEF

The term GEM (Global Environmental Multiscale) actually refers to two main types of models: the Global (formerly known as the SEF) and Regional (formerly known as the RFE or EFR). The model is a global spectral system running on NEC SX-6 supercomputers at the CMC computing facility in Dorval, Quebec.

The GEM Global model forecasts out to 72 hours (12Z base time), 240 hours (00Z base time), and 360 hours (Saturdays). It uses the 3DVAR analysis scheme.

The GEM Regional model is a variable-gridpoint model that produces output from a base time of 00Z and 12Z, forecasting out to 48 hours.

Canada's technological developments began in 1950 with the introduction of an experimental barotropic model running on an IBM 650 at McGill University. Operational charts did not begin until July 1963 when a barotropic model began producing output for 500 mb.

On 18 February 1976 the first global spectral model was implemented. It featured 20 hemispheric waves with rhomboidal truncation and five vertical levels. In 1987 CMC acquired a Cray X/MP 28 for its model suite.

On 22 April 1986, the first regional model, analogous to the NGM and Eta, was introduced. It was called the RFE (Regional Finite Element), also known as EFR (Éléments Finis Régionaux) and featured 15 layers with 190 km resolution, and was placed on the Cray X/MP in 1987 with better resolution.

On 24 February 1997 the RFE became the GEM Regional model, and on 14 October 1998 the SEF was decommissioned. It was replaced by the GEM Global model, a 0.9-deg global uniform grid model with 28 eta levels.

MODEL BIASES

The GEM uses sigma coordinates, and as a result it has difficulties handling lee-mountain effects such as lee cyclogenesis and cold air damming. The GEM model has also been faulted in rejecting too much upper air data which appear to be valid but don't fit the first-guess fields.

Otherwise, very little information has been published on the subjective biases of the GEM model.

Great sites with real-time data for this product . . .
❍ CMC Canada — **weatheroffice.ec.gc.ca/model_forecast**

■ The GEM Global is a spectral model which uses a 0.9-deg uniform lat-long grid. The GEM Regional uses a 354 x 415 point global grid, with 270 x 353 centered on Canada and surrounding regions. All use 28 hybrid sigma-Z surfaces.

■ CMC refers to the GEM as using an eta coordinate system, however this does not share the same definition as that used by the NCEP Eta model.

■ **Model milestones**

GEM GLOBAL

Date	Type	Wave	Res	Lyrs
1976	Spectral	R20	663 km	5
1977	Spectral	R29	458 km	5
1978	Spectral	R20	663 km	10
1981	Spectral	R29	458 km	13
1984	Spectral	T59	225 km	15
1991	Spectral	T79	168 km	21
1993	Spectral	T119	111 km	21
1995	Spectral	T199	67 km	21
1998	Grid	—	0.9°	28

GEM REGIONAL

Date	Type	Wave	Res	Lyrs
1986	-	-	190 km	15
1987	-	-	152 km	15
1988	-	-	100 km	19
1992	-	-	100 km	23
1993	-	-	50 km	25
1996	-	-	35 km	28
1997 Feb 24 - RFE name discontinued				
1998	-	-	24 km	28
2000?	-	-	16 km	35

■ **Operational supercomputers**

1962 (Fall) — Bendix G-20
1967-68 (Sept) — IBM 360/65
1973-75 — Cyber 7600
1977 — Nova
1983 — Cray 1S/1300
1986 (17 Dec) — Cray X-MP/28
1989 — Cray X-MP/416
1992 — NEC SX-3/44/ 4
1995 — NEC SX-3R/44
1996 — NEC SX-4/96M3
1999 — NEC SX-5/32M2
2002 — NEC SX-6

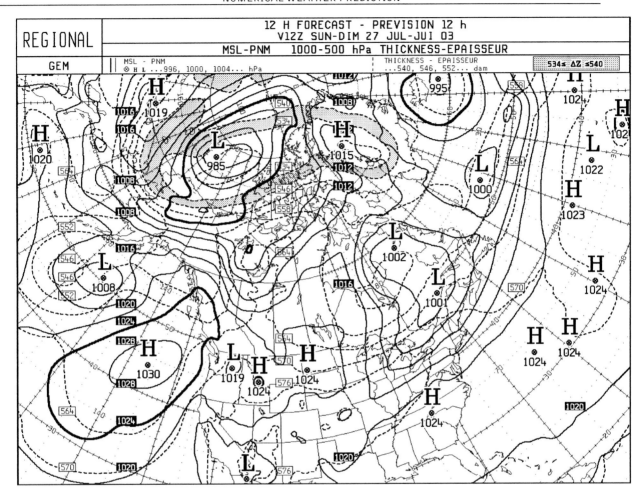

Above: Environment Canada provides an excellent counterpart to the legacy NCEP DIFAX style at <weatheroffice.ec.gc.ca>. *(CMC)*

Right: The global grid of the GEM Global Spectral Model, with the nested domain that makes up the Regional Spectral Model. This smaller grid covers all but the extreme southern United States. *(CMC)*

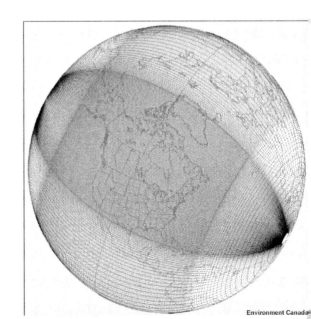

JMA Model (Japan)

The term JMA in American forecasting use usually refers to the global spectral model (JMA/GSM), which yields worldwide coverage. Japan also operates five other models including a regional spectral model (JMA/RSM), a mesoscale model (JMA/MSM), and a typhoon model (JMA/TYM).

Japan began its numerical weather prediction efforts in 1959. The first global-scale spectral model came online in March 1988 using sigma coordinates, but this was rapidly changed to hybrid coordinates in November 1989. Hybrid coordinates follow terrain near the surface, gradually following pressure surfaces in the upper troposphere. New physics packages were added in March 1996, December 1999, and March 2001.

MODEL BIASES

Very little information has been published on subjective biases in the JMA mode. During the author's year of forecasting in Korea, the JMA was noted to have significant skill over the NOGAPS model with nearly all types of weather systems and regimes. However this was in 1996 and the models have undergone changes since then which could affect the impact of this assessment.

Great sites with real-time data for this product . . .
○ Wright Weather ($) (US/Canada) — **www.wright-weather.com**
○ Wetterzentrale (Europe) — **www.wetterzentrale.de/topkarten**

■ The JMA global spectral model is a 213-wave spectral model with triangular truncation. It uses 40 hybrid sigma-pressure levels, with sigma (terrain-following) surfaces near the ground changing to pressure surfaces above the middle troposphere.

■ The JMA hybrid vertical coordinate scheme is also used by the ECMWF, NOGAPS, and UKMET models.

■ The JMA regional spectral model features a resolution of 20 km and uses 40 hybrid layers.

■ **Model milestones**

JMA GLOBAL SPECTRAL

Date	Type	Wave	Res	Lyrs
1988	Spectral	T63	316 km	16
1989	Spectral	T106	188 km	21
1996	Spectral	T213	93 km	30
2001	Spectral	T213	93 km	40

■ **Supercomputers**
1959 — IBM 704
1960-1991 — ?
1992 — NEC SX-3/14/ 1
1993 — Hitachi S-3800/180/ 1
1995 — Hitachi S-3800/480/ 4
1999 — Hitachi SR8000/36/ 36
2001 — Hitachi SR8000/MPP/ 1152

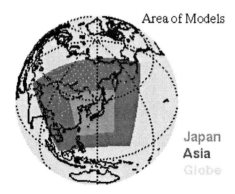

Area of Models

Japan
Asia
Globe

Left: Crude diagram of domains for the JMA Global, Regional, and Spectral models. Very little operational information is available on the JMA models, compared to the American and European counterparts. The language barrier is one root cause. *(JMA)*

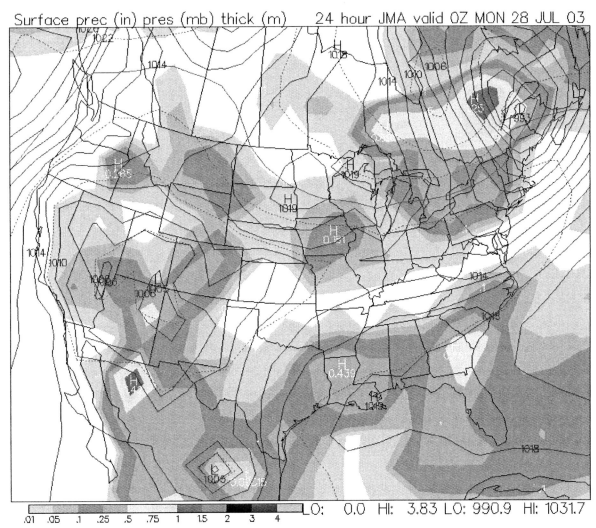

Surface prec (in) pres (mb) thick (m)   24 hour JMA valid 0Z MON 28 JUL 03

.01 .05 .1 .25 .5 .75 1 1.5 2 3 4   LO: 0.0 HI: 3.83 LO: 990.9 HI: 1031.7

Above: Output for the United States from the Japanese JMA Global Spectral Model (JMA/GSM) as obtained at Wright-Weather <www.wright-weather.com>. Output is generally available from 00 to 168 hours for North America. Sources for other regions are not known. *(Wright-Weather)*

Right: The domain and topography of the JMA Regional Spectral Model (JMA/RSM). *(JMA)*

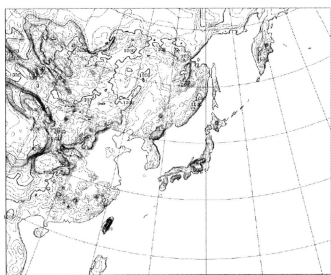

TEXT DATA

SYNOP Surface Observation Format

The SYNOP format is given in WMO Pub. 306, "Manual on Codes" in section FM-12. It specifies the format that must be used worldwide for all non-aviation weather observations (aviation reports are coded under METAR format).

The format is as follows:

AAXX *hhmmw*
CCCCC rxhvv NDDFF 1sttt 2SDDD 3pppp 4PPPP 5appp 6RRRT 7wwpp 8NLMH 9hhmm

If any particular group is missing, it is assumed the category is not applicable. For example, if the sky is clear, the 8*NLMH* cloud code group will be omitted. Solidii ("/") usually indicate missing data.

■ **Header (AAXX** *hhmmw*). The header usually appears at the top of a group of reports collected by a single office. It always starts with "AAXX" ("BBXX" indicates a ship report with more elaborate coding standards that are beyond the scope of this book). The time follows in hours (*hh*) and minutes (*mm*). If the wind indicator (*w*) is 0 or 1, winds are in m/s; if 2 or 3 winds are in knots; an even value is estimated and odd is measured.

■ **Station location (***CCCCC***).** This represents the five-digit WMO identifier where the weather was observed.

■ **Miscellaneous and visibility group (***rxhvv***).** The precipitation indicator (*r*) tells whether a supplementary block is used. Station type (*x*) is 1-3 if manned, 4-7 if automated. Lowest cloud height (*h*) is a coded value. Visibility (*vv*) is also a coded value; when below 50 it generally indicates the visibility in tens of kilometers.

■ **Wind group (***NDDFF***).** This group begins with the total cloud cover (*N*) in eighths; if it is 9 the sky is obscured and if a solidus it is not known. The

wind direction in tens of degrees relative to true north (*dd*) and speed (*ff*) are given. The units are given in the header (see above).

■ **Temperature group (***1sttt***).** Exact temperature (*ttt*) in tens of degrees Celsius. If the sign value (*s*) is "1", the temperature value is negative.

■ **Dewpoint group (***2SDDD***).** Exact dewpoint temperature (*DDD*) in tens of degrees Celsius. If the sign value (*S*) is "1", the dewpoint value is negative.

■ **Station pressure (***3pppp***).** The station pressure (*pppp*) is in tens of millibars.

■ **Sea-level pressure (***4PPPP***).** The sea-level pressure (*pppp*) is in tens of millibars. If the first digit is 1, 2, 5, 7, or 8 this indicates that this is not a sea-level pressure and is instead a geopotential height value.

■ **Sea-level pressure (***5appp***).** Pressure tendency (*a*) with 0-3 risen, 4 steady, and 5-8 fallen, and change (*ppp*) in tens of millibars.

■ **Precipitation (***6RRRT***).** Liquid precipitation amount (*RRR*) in whole mm. "990" is a trace, and with higher values the last digit is the value in tenths of a mm. The duration of the period (*T*) is "4" if 24 hours, "2" if 12 hours, and "1" if 6 hours.

■ **Weather (***7wwpp***).** The current weather (*ww*) and past weather (*pp*) is expressed as a two-digit code (see code table). In general the higher the number the more significant the phenomenon.

■ **Cloud group (***8NLMH***).** The amount of low or middle clouds (*N*) is in eighths. The code for any low (*L*), middle (*M*), or high (*H*) clouds is given.

■ **Time group (***9hhmm***).** The observation time is given in hours (*hh*) and minutes (*mm*) UTC.

409
SMRS15 RUMS 241800
AAXX 24181
22282 32598 71803 10134 20113 40097 56002 85214   333 10163=
22292 32473 61303 10196 20166 40081 56001 85930   333 10241=
22365 NIL=
22438 32571 71802 10182 20165 40105 53003 82274   333 10226=
22446 NIL=
22563 32882 72102 10220 20173 40113 53008 86083   333 10278=
22641 11684 32101 10220 20175 40121 53002 69900 70281 81242   333 10265=
22695 NIL=
22778 11472 79901 10193 20182 40152 52007 69940 70298 82461
333 10274=
22798 12984 71802 10208 20174 40158 54000 69900 85051   333 10275=
22854 11884 31702 10216 20156 40148 57002 60010 70198 81031   333
10236=
22867 11971 21801 10216 20187 40160 57001 69900 70281 80001   333
10242=
22939 32697 21503 10212 20148 40158 53001 81501 333 10272=
22996 12598 60201 10210 20159 40176 53004 69900 83905 333 10280=
27008 32582 72302 10235 20161 40156 57001 87900 333 10284
85920=
27051 32960 82301 10212 20126 40175 53001 80001 333 10268=
27225 33568 22003 10208 20133 40186 53001 82101   333 10262=
27252 NIL=
27369 32581 72702 10222 20158 40191 52004 87300   333 10274 87925=
27393 32598 20000 10224 20144 40189 53001 81401   333 10279=
27479 32599 32401 10225 20153 40193 53006 83200   333 10276=
27532 32997 30000 10198 20149 40193 56001 82031   333 10252=
27648 32997 20000 10192 20155 40203 53002 82030   333 10268=
27679 32980 22302 10232 20100 40198 57006 82040   333 10270=
28214 32996 20000 10203 20141 40192 53003 80008   333 10277=

SMCI07 BABJ 241800 RRA
AAXX 24181
51716 31958 23605 10244 20105 38809 49994 52028 70600 80002
333 00556 10344=
51765 32980 70000 10224 20123 39071 49987 52008 82032 333
00253 10342=
51777 32968 00703 10276 20056 39027 49971 52011 333 00300
10358=
53149 32680 12702 10175 20166 38675 49986 54000 81500 333
00055 10279=
53231 32980 02204 10177 20092 38402 52002 333 00357 10257=
53336 32980 00000 10206 20105 38623 49992 52010 333 00000
10276=

METAR Surface Observation Format

METAR stands for Meteorological Airport Report, and is the worldwide standard for transmitting weather reports from airfields. It is the backbone of weather reports in the United States, Europe, and the Pacific Rim.

Familiarity with METAR format is important for a forecaster to be able to pick up on minor trends that might occur at a weather station. The format is:

CCCC ddhhmmZ (AUTO) dddff VV ww CCCHHH tt/dd P (RMK)

■ **Station location (*CCCC*).** This represents the four-letter ICAO identifier where the weather was observed.
■ **Observation time (*ddhhmmZ*).** The UTC time the observation was taken: calendar day (*dd*); hour (*hh*); and minute (*mm*). The "Z" ending is a reminder that the time zone is Zulu (UTC) time.
■ **Auto flag (AUTO).** If this flag is present, it indicates the observation was taken by a machine.
■ **Wind (*dddff*).** The wind direction in degrees relative to true north (*ddd*) and speed (*ff*). If winds are gusting, the group takes the form *dddffGgg*, where gg is the gust speed. The group is always appended with units: KT (knots), MPS (meters per second) or KMH (km/h). If the wind direction will be variable, *ddd* is encoded as VRB. It is also permissible to encode the group as *dddVddd* to indicate a range of wind directions exceeding 60 degrees.
■ **Prevailing visibility (*VV*).** A number that may be whole or a fraction. Always ends with SM (statute miles) or nothing (meters).
■ **Weather (*ww*).** A two-letter standard abbreviation for any weather that will occur, with appropriate modifiers. The term CAVOK may be used if all clouds are above 5000 ft , visibility is above 10 km, and no significant precipitation is occurring; the United States does not use CAVOK.
■ **Cloud condition (CCCHHH).** Assigned for each cloud layer and may repeat. Consists of cloud cover

(*CCC*) and height in hundreds of feet (*HHH*). Cloud cover may be clear, few (FEW, 1 to 2 eighths coverage), scattered (SCT, 3 to 4 eighths), broken (BKN, 5 to 7 eighths), or overcast (OVC). When the sky is obscured, *CCC* will be encoded as VV for vertical visibility and the *HHH* value will indicate the visibility into the obscuration.
■ **Temperature/dewpoint (*tt/dd*).** The temperature (*tt*) and dewpoint (*dd*) in whole degrees Celsius. If any value is negative, it is preceded by an "M".
■ **Pressure (*P*).** If this value starts with "A", it indicates altimeter setting with the value in hundreds of inches. If the value starts with "Q" it indicates sea-level pressure with the value in whole millibars.
■ **Remarks (RMK).** If the word "RMK" appears, it indicates that supplementary information follows. Here are some of the more common remarks:
- A01 or A02. Automated station
- SLP*ppp*. Sea-level pressure, where *ppp* is the tens, units, and tenths value in millibars.
- T*atttbdddd*. Exact temperature (*tttt*) and dewpoint (*dddd*) in tens of degrees Celsius. The elements *a* and *b* are sign flags: when it is "1" the value that follows it is negative.
- 1*xxxx*. Six-hour max temperature (*xxxx*) in tens of degrees Celsius.
- 2*nnnn*. Six-hour minimum temperature (*nnnn*) in tens of degrees Celsius.
- 4/*sss*. Snow depth (*sss*)in whole inches.
- 4*axxxbnnn*. Twenty-four hour maximum (*xxx*) and minimum (*nnn*) temperature in tens of degrees Celsius. The elements *a* and *b* are sign flags: when it is "1" the value that follows it is negative.
- 5*tppp*. Pressure tendency (*t*) with 0-3 risen, 4 steady, and 5-8 fallen, and change (*ppp*) in tens of millibars.
- 6*pppp*. Six-hour precipitation (*pppp*) in hundreds of inches.
- 7*pppp*. Twenty-four hour precipitation (*pppp*) in hundreds of inches.
- 8/*mh*. Cloud type codes.
- PCPN *pppp* or P *pppp*. One-hour precipitation (*pppp*) in hundreds of inches.

Great sites with real-time data for this product . . .
○ NWS — **weather.noaa.gov/weather/taf.shtml**
○ NWS — **www.nws.noaa.gov/radar**
○ Weathertap ($) — **www.weathertap.com**

2003/07/24 08:00
LPMT 240800Z 34009KT 9999 SCT018 21/17 Q1021 BLU

2003/07/24 08:00
LPOV 240800Z 33002KT 8000 BKN020 BKN080 19/16 Q1022 WHT

2003/07/24 08:00
LPST 240800Z 35009KT 9999 FEW008 BKN013 20/15 Q1023 GRN/WHT

2003/07/24 08:20
ESNU 240820Z 31006KT CAVOK 21/10 Q1012

2003/07/24 08:00
OIIP 240800Z 15005MPS 6000 SCT200 31/12 Q1007

2003/07/24 07:50
LTCG 240750Z 27013KT 9999 SCT035TCU BKN100 26/21 Q1010 NOSIG RMK RWY29
29014KT

2003/07/24 08:10
MYEG 240810Z AUTO 10007KT 10SM OVC001 27/23 A3004 RMK AO2 LTG DSNT NW

2003/07/24 08:20
EKAH 240820Z 14005KT 090V250 9999 FEW012 SCT160 20/16 Q1014

2003/07/24 08:20
EKBI 240820Z 11003KT 8000 FEW030TCU BKN060 17/16 Q1014

2003/07/24 08:24
KBKV 240824Z AUTO 00000KT 1 3/4SM BR CLR 21/21 A3002 RMK AO2 $

2003/07/24 08:24
KUUU 240824Z AUTO VRB06KT 10SM BKN011 BKN022 21/20 A2996 RMK AO2 RAE07 P0001

2003/07/24 08:24
PAQT 240824Z AUTO 02008KT 3SM -RA BR OVC002 09/08 A2969 RMK AO2 RAB06 TSNO
PNO $

2003/07/24 08:00
FCBB 240800Z 23004KT 180V270 4000 BR BKN020 22/19 Q1017 BECMG 5000

2003/07/24 08:00
UUYS 240800Z 17006MPS CAVOK 16/04 Q1017 NOSIG RMK QFE756 14CLRD60

Terminal Aerodrome Forecast (TAF)

The Terminal Aerodrome Forecast (TAF) is the worldwide standard for encoding standardized forecasts for any airport. It is based on the METAR observation format. For many decades the United States used domestic FT (terminal forecast) style, an extension of their SAO airways observation format. Both the FT and SAO formats were discontinued after a 1993-1995 transition period, and are now historical relics.

A TAF forecast can be particularly useful to meteorologists to ascertain what is expected at another location. The general format is as follows:

CCCC ddhhmm DDHHEE dddff VV ww CCCHHH

■ **Station location (*CCCC*).** This represents the four-letter ICAO identifier where the forecasted weather will occur.
■ **Issuance time (*ddhhmm*).** The UTC time the forecast was issued. The calendar day (*dd*); hour (*hh*); and minute (*mm*). A "Z" may be suffixed to the end as a reminder it is Zulu (UTC) time.
■ **Forecast period (*DDHHEE*).** The UTC time of the forecast period, with the starting day (*DD*) and hour (*HH*), and the ending hour (*EE*) (usually on the next day).
■ **Wind (*dddff*).** The wind direction in degrees relative to true north (*ddd*) and speed (*ff*). If winds are gusting, the group takes the form *dddffGgg*, where *gg* is the gust speed. The group is always appended with units: KT (knots), MPS (meters per second) or KMH (km/h). If the wind direction will be variable, *ddd* is encoded as VRB. It is also permissible to encode the group as *dddNddd* to indicate a range of wind directions exceeding 60 degrees.
■ **Prevailing visibility (*VV*).** A number that may be whole or a fraction. Always ends with SM (statute miles) or nothing (meters).
■ **Weather (*ww*).** A two-letter standard abbreviation for any weather that will occur, with appropriate modifiers. The term CAVOK may be used if all clouds are above 5000 ft , visibility is above 10 km, and no significant precipitation is occurring; the United States does not use CAVOK.
■ **Cloud code group (*CCCHHH*).** Assigned for each cloud layer and may repeat. Consists of cloud cover (*CCC*) and height in hundreds of feet (*HHH*). Cloud cover may be clear, few (FEW, 1 to 2 eighths coverage), scattered (SCT, 3 to 4 eighths), broken (BKN, 5 to 7 eighths), or overcast (OVC). When the sky is obscured, *CCC* will be encoded as VV for vertical visibility and the *HHH* value will indicate the visibility into the obscuration.
■ **Wind shear group (WS*hhh*/*dddff*).** Sometimes, particularly in the United States, a low-level wind shear alert will be encoded. The value *hhh* specifies the maximum height above the surface in hundreds of feet, and *ddd* and *ff* specify the wind direction and speed above that height.
■ **Transition identifier.** These introduce new groups of weather conditions that will occur.
- FM *hhmm* indicates a significant change will take place at hour *hh* and minute *mm*.
- TEMPO *hhee* indicates a temporary condition lasting a total of less than half the time period will occur between hour *hh* and hour *ee*.
- BECMG *hhee* indicates a transition period that will begin at hour *hh* and end at hour *ee*, and after this time the new condition will become predominant.
- PROB*pp* *hhee* indicates a temporary condition with a probability value. The probability in percent is *pp*, and the duration of the expected weather ranges from hour *hh* to hour *ee*. This is used primarily in the United States. Only 30 or 40 is used; if there is a higher probability, then TEMPO is used.
■ **Other groups.** The U.S. military tends to use two groups:
- QNH*pppp*INS, where *pppp* is the lowest expected altimeter setting in hundreds of inches. This is used by U.S. military stations.
- T*tt*/*hh*Z is a maximum and minimum temperature group for the forecast period (two groups are used), where *tt* is the temperature and *hh* is the hour of occurrence. The group may also appear as TN*tt*/*hh*Z TX*tt*/*hh*Z.

```
2003/07/23 23:38
KJFK 232338Z 240024 18012G22KT 6SM BR SCT025 BKN050
     TEMPO 0004 4SM -SHRA BR OVC035
     FM0400 19012KT 4SM BR VCSH SCT020 BKN040
     TEMPO 0408 2SM SHRA BR OVC010
     FM0800 20009KT 3SM BR VCSH OVC015
     TEMPO 0812 1 1/2SM BR OVC008
     FM1200 20010KT 5SM BR BKN025
     FM1800 20012KT P6SM VCTS SCT025CB BKN050


2003/07/24 03:00
HTZA 240300Z 240606 17010KT 9999 SCT018 PROB 30 TEMPO 0608
     9000 -SHRA BKN016 SCT080 BECMG 1114 09015G20KT 9999 SCT020
     BECMG 1623 09010KT FEW018 BECMG 0005 13006KT SCT015


2003/07/24 04:00
HEMM 240400Z 240606 VRB03KT 6000 SKC FM0700 34014KT 9999 FEW020


2003/07/24 03:00
VECC 240300Z 240606 12008KT 4000 HZ SCT015 BKN090
     BECMG 1112 12006KT 3000 HZ
     BECMG 1618 VRB03KT 2000 HZ
     BECMG 0203 12005KT 3000 HZ
     BECMG 0506 12008KT 4000 HZ
     TEMPO 0606 1500 TSRA/RA SCT008 FEW025CB OVC080


2003/07/24 04:12
BIRK 240412Z 240606 22005KT 9999 SCT020 BKN040 BECMG 1518
          33008KT PROB40 TEMPO 1521 -SHRA BKN015 BECMG 2124
          33015KT 9000 -RA BKN015 OVC030


2003/07/24 04:00
UAAA 240400Z 240606 26005MPS 9999 BKN050CB BKN100
     TEMPO 0609 TS
     TEMPO 0913 VRB12MPS TSSHRA SQ
     TEMPO 1318 TSRA
     TEMPO 1822 SHRA


2003/07/24 04:26
RODN 240404 16010KT 9999 VCTS SCT010 SCT025CB SCT035 BKN250
     QNH2994INS
     TEMPO 0405 25010G15KT 4800 -TSRA SCT010 BKN025CB
     OVC035
     BECMG 1314 16010KT 9999 NSW SCT025 BKN250 QNH2994INS
     BECMG 0203 28010G15KT 4800 -TSRA SCT010 BKN025CB
     BKN035 QNH2994INS T34/06Z T28/21Z
```

Radiosonde Observation Format

Nearly all radiosonde data is transmitted in the TEMP format prescribed by the WMO in Publication 306, Section FM-35. It is broken up into three major blocks, TTAA (significant level), TTBB (mandatory level), and PPBB (winds aloft) data. Other blocks such as TTCC and TTDD pertain to data in the stratosphere and is not generally used by forecasters.

■ **Mandatory level block (TTAA).** This block shows wind, temperature, and dewpoint at predesignated levels, such as 200 and 500 mb.

The block usually begins with:

TTAA *ddhhi cccc*

The TTAA is a flag that shows this is the mandatory level block. Then follows the calendar day (*dd*) and hour (*hh*). A value of 50 is added to the day if the wind units are in knots, otherwise the wind units are in m/s. The highest wind data (*i*) is a coded figure which is roughly in hundreds of millibars. Finally the WMO station identifier (*cccc*) is indicated.

Following this is a series of repeating blocks in the format:

pphhh TTTDD dddff

The level (*pp*) is expressed in tens of millibars, e.g. "85" indicates 850 mb. The exception is "99", which always is the first block and indicates the ground, and "92", which is 925 mb, and "88" and "77" are special use (see below). Following this is the height (*hhh*) in different expressions of meters, except for level "99" (ground) in which *hhh* is the surface pressure in tens, units, and tenths of a millibar. The *hhh* expression is in whole meters from 1000 to 700 mb (it is 1*hhh* meters at 850 mb and 2*hhh* or 3*hhh* meters at 700 mb, whichever brings it closer to 3000 m). From 500 to 400 mb *hhh* is expressed in decameters. From 300 to 100 mb *hhh* is 1*hhh* decameters. Following this is the temperature block *TTTDD*, with temperature (*TTT*) in tens of degrees Celsius and dewpoint depression (*DD*) in units and tenths of degrees Celsius if at or below

"50" and in whole degrees Celsius if above "50" (subtract 50 before using). Finally the wind is presented as direction (*ddd*) relative to true north and speed (*ff*). Direction always ends with "0" or "5", and "1" is added to it for each hundred units of wind speed (e.g. a *dddff* of 25604 indicates a wind from 255° at a speed of 104).

Tropopause information is encoded as **88***ppp* **TTTDD** *dddff* which indicates conditions at the tropopause: most importantly its pressure. Maximum winds are encoded as **77***ppp dddff*.

■ **Significant level block (TTBB).** The significant level block is designed to show temperature and dewpoint only at levels bounded by strong changes. The header and format is much the same as the mandatory level (TTAA) block, except that the repeating data block is in the format:

nnppp TTTDD

where *nn* occurs in a repeating sequence (00 for the surface, followed by 11, 22, 33, 44, 55, 66, 77, 88, 99, 11, 22, etc). The rest of the block is identical to the TTAA block with the omission of wind data, and no tropopause or maximum wind data.

■ **Winds aloft block (PPBB).** This block contains wind data only, and it is graduated in feet rather than millibars. Again, the header and format are similar to TTAA and TTBB format, except that repeating data is in the format:

9habc aaaAA bbbBB cccCC

The "9" is a marker that makes it easy to pick out the group elements. The rest of the group 9*habc* indicates heights of the block, followed by wind data *aaaAA bbbBB cccCC* (encoded the same way as in the TTAA/TTBB sections) at three levels. The ten-thousands place for height is indicated by *h* and the thousands place for each of the three groups by *a*, *b*, and *c*. The height value *ha*000 ft applies to wind group *aaaAA*, *hb*000 ft applies to wind group *bbbBB*, and *hc*000 ft applies to wind group *cccCC*. Not all three groups need to be encoded; if one or two are omitted, *a*, *b*, or *c* will contain a solidus.

Great sites with real-time data for this product . . .
❍ SUNY Albany — **www.atmos.albany.edu/weather/data1/upperair**

520
USUS50 KWBC 241200 RRC

TTAA 74121 72318 99944 13606 26005 00145 ///// ///// 92814 14421
28513 85525 12657 30015 70126 02256 25526 50577 13563 24026 40743
23777 23056 30948 36173 22089 25072 44569 22101 20218 55167 21602
15401 55770 22556 10657 60771 21021 88183 56767 22083 77262 22105
41606 51515 10164 00004 10194 30015 27018=

647
UMUS41 KRNK 241217
SGLRNK

72318 TTBB 74120 72318 00944 13606 11931 14822 22877 11624
33869 13057 44850 12657 55700 02256 66631 01763 77620 02760
88578 05563 99509 12561 11470 17165 22430 19981 33196 55966
44112 56772 55100 60771 31313 45202 81106 41414 50961=

PPBB 74120 72318 90034 26005 30518 31517 90678 28515 28016
25517 909// 25522 91124 25523 25020 23519 916// 24023 92058
24525 23059 22582 93045 22587 22105 22102 9404/ 21602 22068
95024 22536 23528 21521=

445
USRE01 FMEE 241200

TTAA 74111 61976 99017 26260 12019 00157 22857 12021 92830 17025
12528 85548 13014 13032 70166 11091 14020 50590 04384 11515 40761
16179 10512 30972 30974 10509 25098 415// 04504 20246 537// 00514
15424 677// 02065 10662 807// 24508 88999 77149 02066 31313 47408
81059=

519
UKRE01 FMEE 241200

TTBB 74118 61976 00017 26260 11009 23458 22968 20034 33947 18229
44788 09205 55774 12459 66758 12091 77725 11091 88672 11291 99588
03086 11548 00885 22443 11380 33339 23776 44257 40171 55164 643//
66147 685// 77137 669// 88102 799// 21212 00017 12019 11867 12534
22803 14028 33766 11523 44702 14520 55641 12508 66555 13517 77443
09013 88328 13011 99216 00000 11149 02066 22142 01556 33/// /////
44118 30006 55104 18508 31313 47408 81059 41414 48501 51515 92830
17025 12528 77318 12258 12024 60439 04286 13012=

APPENDIX

Appendix 1A. Surface Plot Schematic

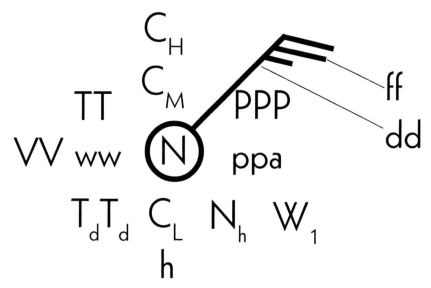

Presented here is the universally-adopted surface plot form.

TT — Temperature in degrees Celsius or Fahrenheit. Usually in whole degrees but may be expressed in tenths.

VV — Visibility in statute miles or meters. Mile values will appear as either whole numbers or fractional numbers. Meter values frequently appear as four digits, e.g. 0700.

ww — Symbol for weather type (see Table XXXX).

T_dT_d — Dewpoint temperature in degrees Celsius or Fahrenheit. Usually in whole degrees but may be expressed in tenths.

C_H — High cloud symbol.

C_M — Middle cloud symbol.

N — Total amount of cloud cover in oktas (eighths). The amount of the circle filled in is proportional to the amount of cloud cover. ○=Clear; ◑=1 okta; ◐=2 oktas; ◑=3 oktas; ◑=4 oktas; ◕=5 oktas; ◕=6 oktas; ◕=7 oktas; ●=8 oktas; ⊗=Sky obscured. When an automated station produced the observation, the symbol will be plotted as a square instead of a circle. Coloring may optionally be used: blue indicates MVFR flying conditions (ceiling 1000-3000 and/or visibility 3-5 sm); and red for IFR flying conditions (ceiling less than 1000 ft and/or visibility less than 3 miles).

C_L — Low cloud symbol.

h — Height of lowest low cloud layer, or if not present, lowest middle cloud layer. This is a coded single-digit value. 0=0-50 m; 1=50-100 m; 2=100-200 m; 3=200-300 m; 4=300-600m; 5=600-1000 m; 6=1000-1500 m; 7=1500-200 m; 8=2000-2500 m; 9=2500+ m; /=unknown.

PPP — Pressure in tens, units, and tenths of a millibar. Sometimes shows units, tenths, and hundredths of an inch of mercury.

pp — 3-hour pressure change in units and tenths of a millibar.

a — A two-segmented line representing pressure change during the past three-hours.

N_h — Amount of lowest low cloud layer, or if not present, lowest middle cloud layer. Expressed in oktas (eighths); if 9 the sky is obscured.

W_1 — Symbol for type of recent weather (See Table XXXX).

dd — Wind direction. Shaft points into the wind.

ff — Wind speed. A thick flag represents 50 kt, a long barb represents 10 kt, and each short barb represents 5 kt. The example shows 25 kt. If the wind is calm, the shaft is omitted and a circle is drawn around the station plot.

Appendix 1B. Upper Air Plot Schematic

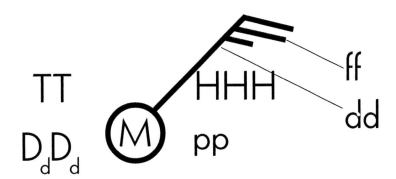

Presented here is the universally-adopted upper air plot form.

TT — Temperature in degrees Celsius. Usually in whole degrees but may be expressed in tenths.

D_dD_d — Dewpoint depression in Celsius degrees. Usually in whole degrees but may be expressed in tenths.

M — The plot circle is filled whenever the dewpoint depression is 5 Celsius degrees or less. This signifies the possible presence of cloud material and perhaps the threat for icing. The element will appear as a square when the observation was made by an aircraft (such as ACARS data) or a dropsonde. It will appear as an asterisk when the observation was satellite-based.

HHH — Geopotential height. It is either thousands, hundreds, and tens of meters or hundreds, tens, and units of meters according to the level involved. See the table at right.

pp — 12-hour height change in meters.

dd — Wind direction. Shaft points into the wind.

ff — Wind speed. A thick flag represents 50 kt, a long barb represents 10 kt, and each short barb represents 5 kt. The example shows 25 kt. If the wind is calm, the shaft is omitted and a circle is drawn around the station plot.

HEIGHT DECODING RULES

1000 mb: Geopotential height is a whole number in hundreds, tens, and units of meters. If the figure exceeds 500, subtract it from 500 to get the correct negative height.

925 mb: Geopotential height is a whole number in hundreds, tens, and units of meters.

850 mb: Geopotential height is in hundreds, tens, and units of meters. The thousands place is always "1".

700 mb: Geopotential height is in hundreds, tens, and units of meters. The thousands place is always "2" or "3", whichever brings the entire figure closest to 3,000.

500 mb, 400 mb: Geopotential height is in thousands, hundreds, and tens of meters. In other words, it is an expression in whole decameters.

300 mb, 250 mb: Geopotential height is in thousands, hundreds, and tens of meters. The ten-thousands place is always "0" or "1", whichever brings the entire figure closest to 10,000.

200 mb, 150 mb, 100 mb: Geopotential height is in thousands, hundreds, and tens of meters. The ten-thousands place is "1".

Appendix 2A. ICAO Regions

An ICAO identifier tells much more than you might expect, even when you don't know where the station is. The first digit always indicates the geographic region of the station. The second digit, in some cases, indicates the country or sub-region of the station. *(Source: ICAO Document 7910, Location Indicators)*

Loc	Region		Examples
Axxx	Antarctica, New Guinea, Solomon Islands	AYPY	Port Moresby, Papua New Guinea
Bxxx	Greenland and Iceland	BIRK	Reykjavik, Iceland
Cxxx	Canada	CYYZ	Toronto, Ontario
Dxxx	Northwest Africa	DNMM	Lagos, Nigeria
Exxx	Northern Europe	EHAM	Amsterdam, Netherlands
Fxxx	Southern and Central Africa	FACT	Capetown, South Africa
Gxxx	West Africa & East Atlantic	GMTT	Tangier, Morocco
Hxxx	East Africa	HECA	Cairo, Egypt
Kxxx	United States	KJFK	New York City, New York
Lxxx	Southern Europe	LIRF	Rome, Italy
Mxxx	Central America and West Caribbean	MMMX	Mexico City, Mexico
Nxxx	South Pacific	NZAA	Auckland, New Zealand
Oxxx	Middle East	OIII	Teheran, Iran
Pxxx	North Pacific, Alaska, and Hawaii	PANC	Anchorage, Alaska
Rxxx	Western Pacific	RJAA	Tokyo, Japan
Sxxx	South America	SAEZ	Buenos Aires, Argentina
Txxx	Atlantic and East Caribbean	TJSJ	San Juan, Puerto Rico
Uxxx	Former Soviet Republics	UUEE	Moscow
Vxxx	India and Indochina	VIDP	Delhi, India
Wxxx	Indonesia, Malaysia, and Singapore	WSSS	Singapore
Yxxx	Australia	YSSY	Sydney, Australia
Zxxx	China, Mongolia, and North Korea	ZBAA	Beijing, China

Appendix 2B. WMO Regions

WMO station numbers are used primarily in SYNOP surface reports and in TEMP upper air observations. As with ICAO identifers, a WMO identifier can reveal some information about its location, as the first and second digits relate the station to a geographic area. *(Source: WMO Pub. 9, Vol A - Observing Stations)*

Loc	Region	Examples
0xxxx	Northwest Europe	07150 - Paris, France
1xxxx	Southeast Europe	16240 - Rome, Italy
2xxxx	Northern former USSR	27515 - Moscow, Russia
3xxxx	Southern former USSR	38457 - Tashkent, Uzbekistan
4xxxx	Middle East and Pacific Rim	47662 - Tokyo, Japan
5xxxx	China	54511 - Beijing, China
6xxxx	Africa	61641 - Dakar, Senegal
7xxxx	North America	72530 - Chicago, United States
8xxxx	South America	83378 - Brasilia, Brazil
9xxxx	Australasia	94767 - Sydney, Australia

Appendix 3. Descriptors

These are the standardized weather and obscuration to vision t ypes used in METAR and TAF forecasts. Only the SYNOP code format, containing up to 99 weather types, goes into further detail. The basic construction is in the order **intensity-proximity-precipitation-(space)-obscuration-miscellaneous**. Therefore freezing rain with fog is encoded as FZRA FG. All precipitation is assumed to be moderate unless a different intensity modifier (+ or -) is used. *(Source: WMO Pub 306, Manual on Codes: Code Table 4678)*

Abbv	Meaning	Type of item	Abbv	Meaning	Type of item
-	Light	Intensity	MI	Shallow	Descriptor
+	Heavy	Intensity	PE	Ice pellets (sleet)	*DISCONTINUED*
BC	Patches	Descriptor	PL	Ice pellets (sleet)	Precipitation
BL	Blowing	Descriptor	PO	Dust devils	Miscellaneous
BR	Mist	Obscuration	PR	Partial	Descriptor
DR	Drifting	Descriptor	PY	Spray	Obscuration
DS	Dust storm	Miscellaneous	RA	Rain	Precipitation
DU	Widespread dust	Obscuration	SA	Sand	Obscuration
DZ	Drizzle	Precipitation	SG	Snow Grains	Precipitation
FC	Funnel cloud	Miscellaneous	SH	Shower	Descriptor
FG	Fog	Obscuration	SN	Snow	Precipitation
FU	Smoke	Obscuration	SQ	Wind squalls	Miscellaneous
FZ	Freezing	Descriptor	SS	Sandstorm	Miscellaneous
GR	Hail	Precipitation	TS	Thunder	Descriptor
GS	Small hail	Precipitation	UP	Unknown precip	Precipitation
HZ	Haze	Obscuration	VA	Volcanic ash	Obscuration
IC	Ice crystals	Precipitation	VC	In vicinity	Proximity

Appendix 4. Present Weather

These two-digit numerical codes indicate the type of present weather that exists. They are used in SYNOP reports. The format is laid down in WMO Pub. 306, "Manual on Codes".

Code	Sym	Meaning
00		Clear skies
01		Clouds dissolving
02		State of the sky unchanged
03		Clouds developing
04	⌐	Smoke
05	∞	Haze
06	S	Widespread dust not raised by wind
07	$	Dust or sand raised by wind
08	ၔ	Dust devils
09	(S)	Duststorm or sandstorm not at station
10	=	Mist
11	⁼⁼	Patches of shallow fog
12	⁼⁼	Continuous shallow fog
13	<	Lightning visible, no thunder heard
14	⦁	Virga
15	)•(	Distant precipitation
16	(•)	Nearby precipitation
17	(R)	Thunderstorm with no precipitation
18	∀	Wind squall
19	) (	Funnel cloud, waterspout, or tornado
20	⁀]	Drizzle during past hour
21	•]	Rain during past hour
22	•]	Snow during past hour
23	⁀]	Rain and snow during past hour
24	~]	Freezing rain during past hour
25	⍦]	Rain showers during past hour
26	⍦]	Snow showers during past hour
27	⍦]	Hail showers during past hour
28	≡]	Fog during past hour
29	R]	Thunderstorm during past hour
30	S̵|	Slight-moderate duststorm, decreasing
31	S̵	Slight-moderate duststorm, steady
32	|S̵	Slight-moderate duststorm, increasing
33	S̵|	Severe duststorm, decreasing
34	S̵	Severe duststorm, steady
35	|S̵	Severe duststorm, increasing
36	+	Slight-moderate drifting snow
37	+	Heavy drifting snow
38	+	Slight-moderate blowing snow
39	+	Heavy blowing snow
40	(≡)	Fog at a distance
41	⁼⁼	Patches of fog
42	≡|	Fog, sky visible, thinning
43	≡|	Fog, sky not visible, thinning
44	≡	Fog, sky visible, no change
45	≡	Fog, sky not visible, no change
46	|≡	Fog, sky visible, becoming thicker
47	|≡	Fog, sky not visible, becoming thicker
48	⩜	Fog, depositing rime, sky visible
49	⩜	Fog, depositing rime, sky not visible

Code	Sym	Meaning
50	،	Drizzle, light, intermittent
51	،،	Drizzle, light, continuous
52	؛	Drizzle, moderate, intermittent
53	؛،	Drizzle, moderate, continuous
54	⦂	Drizzle, heavy, intermittent
55	⦂•	Drizzle, heavy, continuous
56	∿	Freezing drizzle, light
57	∿∿	Freezing drizzle, moderate or heavy
58	؛	Drizzle and rain, light
59	؛	Drizzle and rain, moderate or heavy
60	•	Rain, light, intermittent
61	••	Rain, light, continuous
62	⦂	Rain, moderate, intermittent
63	∴	Rain, moderate, continuous
64	⦂	Rain, heavy, intermittent
65	∵	Rain, heavy, continuous
66	∿	Freezing rain, light
67	∿•	Freezing rain, moderate or heavy
68	⦂	Rain and snow, light
69	⦂	Rain and snow, moderate or heavy
70	✳	Snow, light, intermittent
71	✳✳	Snow, light, continuous
72	✻	Snow, moderate, intermittent
73	✻✻	Snow, moderate, continuous
74	✻	Snow, heavy, intermittent
75	✻∵	Snow, heavy, continuous
76	⟷	Diamond dust (ice crystals)
77	⇴	Snow grains
78	⇤	Snow crystals
79	△	Ice pellets
80	▽	Rain showers, light
81	▽	Rain showers, moderate to heavy
82	▽	Rain showers, violent
83	▽	Snow and rain showers, light
84	▽	Snow and rain showers, moderate to heavy
85	▽	Snow showers, light
86	▽	Snow showers, moderate to heavy
87	▽	Snow and ice pellet showers, light
88	▽	Snow and ice pellet showers, mod. to heavy
89	▽	Hail showers, light
90	▽	Hail showers, moderate to heavy
91	R⊦	Recent thunderstorm, light rain
92	R⊧	Recent thunderstorm, mod. to heavy rain
93	R⊦	Recent thunderstorm, light snow or mix
94	R⊧	Recent thunderstorm, mod-heavy snow/mix
95	R	Thunderstorm, light to moderate
96	R	Thunderstorm, light to moderate w/ hail
97	R	Thunderstorm, heavy
98	R	Thunderstorm, heavy, with duststorm
99	R	Thunderstorm, heavy, with hail

Appendix 5. Cloud code groups

These are the code forms used to represent low, middle, and high clouds. They are commonly encoded in both SYNOP and METAR reports. *(Source: WMO Pub 306, Manual on Codes: Code Table ___)*

Low cloud types
1   CUMULUS, fair weather, no vertical development
2   CUMULUS, moderate vertical development
3   CUMULONIMBUS, no anvil
4   STRATOCUMULUS formed by spreading of cumulus
5   STRATOCUMULUS
6   STRATUS, of fair weather
7   STRATUS, of bad weather (scud)
8   CUMULUS AND STRATOCUMULUS with bases at different levels
9   CUMULONIMBUS with anvil cloud
0   No low clouds
/   Low clouds not visible due to darkness or obscuration

Middle cloud types
1   ALTOSTRATUS, mostly transparent
2   ALTOSTRATUS, opaque, or NIMBOSTRATUS
3   ALTOCUMULUS, mostly transparent
4   ALTOCUMULUS, patches
5   ALTOCUMULUS, invading the sky
6   ALTOCUMULUS, formed by spreading of cumulus
7   ALTOCUMULUS, at different layers
8   ALTOCUMULUS, castellanus (cumuliform)
9   ALTOCUMULUS, of a chaotic sky at random levels
0   No middle clouds
/   Middle clouds not visible due to darkness or obscuration

High cloud types
1   CIRRUS, fibrous
2   CIRRUS, in dense patches
3   CIRRUS, from cumulonimbus anvil
4   CIRRUS, progressively invading the sky
5   CIRRUS OR CIRROSTRATUS, invading sky, less than 45 deg above horizon
6   CIRRUS OR CIRROSTRATUS, invading sky, more than 45 deg above horizon
7   CIRROSTRATUS, covering the entire sky
8   CIRROSTRATUS, not covering the entire sky, not invading
9   CIRROCUMULUS
0   No high clouds
/   High clouds not visible due to darkness or obscuration

Appendix 6. Isopleths

What is a line called when it represents a certain quantity? This table will explain the technical name. *(Source: AMS Glossary of Meteorology <amsglossary.allenpress.com/glossary>).*

A line of equal . . .	Term
Temperature	isotherm
Potential temperature (theta)	isentrope
Dewpoint	isodrosotherm
Humidity	isohume
Wind speed	isotach, isovel
Wind direction	isogon
Shear	isoshear
Pressure	isobar
Density	isopycnal, isopycnic
Height	isoheight, contour, isohypse
Cloud cover	isoneph
Time	isochrone
Thunderstorm phase	isobront
Thunderstorm frequency or intensity	isoceraunic
Radar Doppler velocity	isodop
Precipitation	isohyet
Seasonal precipitation	isomer
Snowfall or snow depth	isonival, isochion
Sunlight	isohel
Aurora frequency	isochasm
Radar echo intensity	isoecho

Appendix 7. Chart Analysis Symbology

Shown here are standard markings used by Air Force Global Weather Central during the 1950s and 1960s, as published by Col. Robert C. Miller in *Notes on Analysis and Severe-Storm Forecasting Procedures of the Air Force Global Weather Central* (1972). Miller was a driving force in severe weather forecasting during the 1950s and 1960s and established many of the techniques used in Air Force forecasting during that era. He also created one of the few sets of meteorological symbology ever developed. While some styles have been adopted, many have become technically obsolete, fallen into disuse, or substituted with generic styles. Regardless of the state of modern-day techniques, it can be said that there has been no comparable set of conventions released since Miller's 1972 paper, and they serve as a fascinating reference.

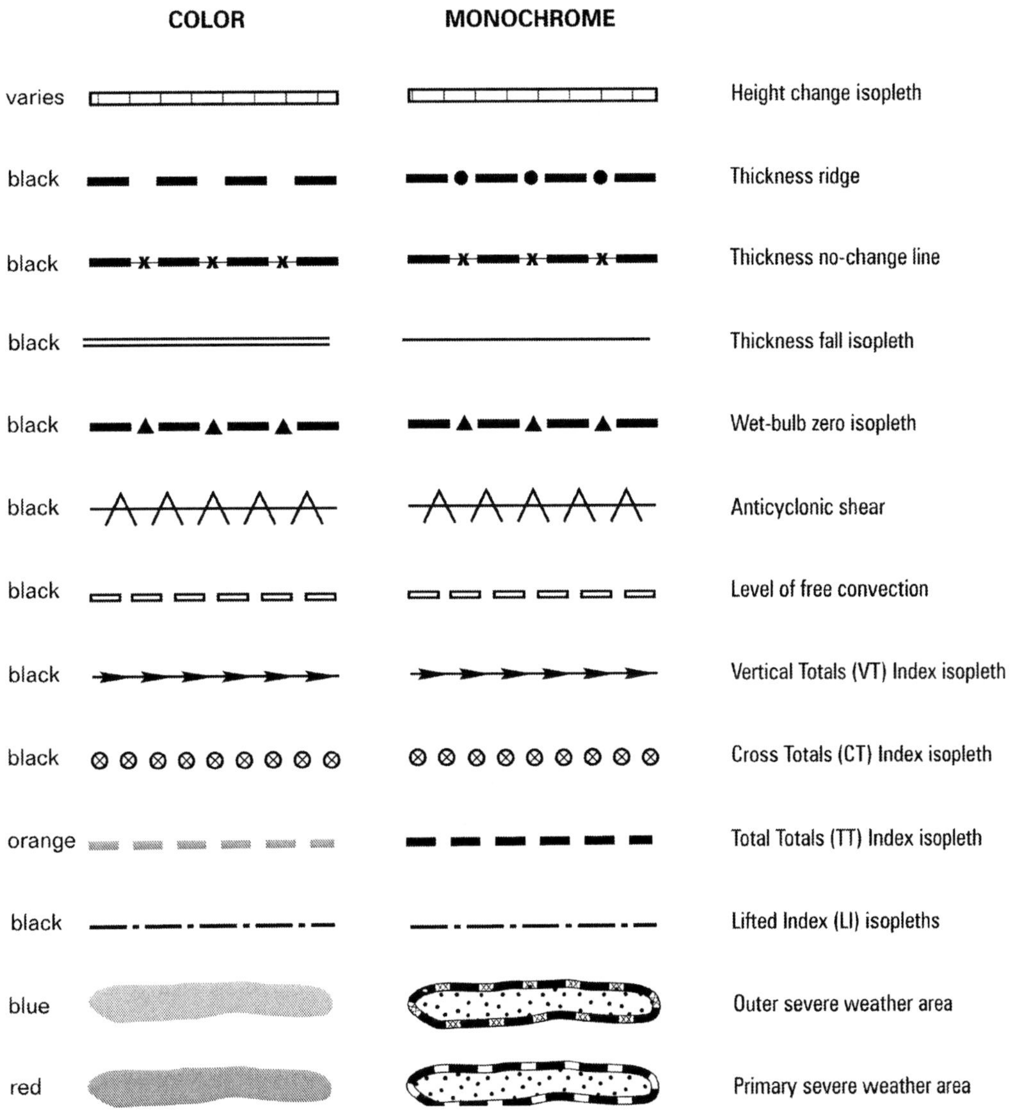

COLOR	MONOCHROME	
varies		Height change isopleth
black		Thickness ridge
black		Thickness no-change line
black		Thickness fall isopleth
black		Wet-bulb zero isopleth
black		Anticyclonic shear
black		Level of free convection
black		Vertical Totals (VT) Index isopleth
black		Cross Totals (CT) Index isopleth
orange		Total Totals (TT) Index isopleth
black		Lifted Index (LI) isopleths
blue		Outer severe weather area
red		Primary severe weather area

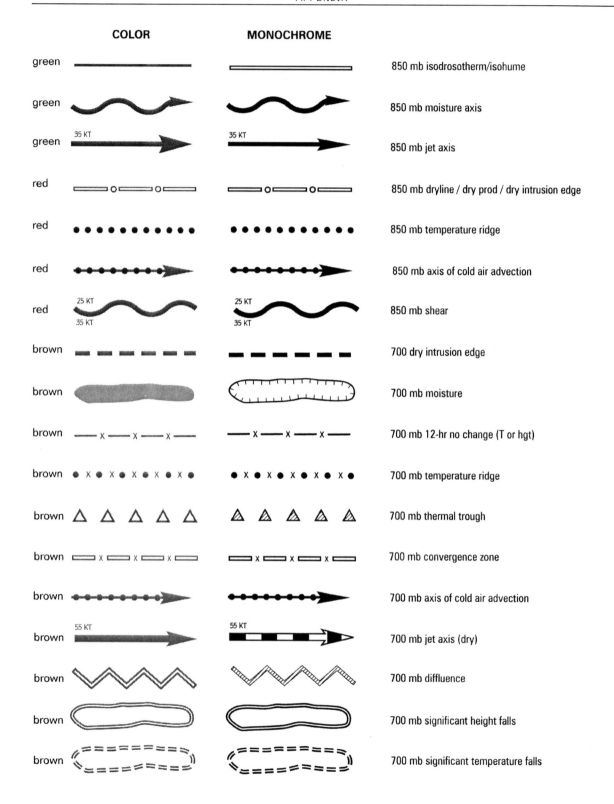

COLOR	MONOCHROME	
green		850 mb isodrosotherm/isohume
green		850 mb moisture axis
green (35 KT)	(35 KT)	850 mb jet axis
red		850 mb dryline / dry prod / dry intrusion edge
red		850 mb temperature ridge
red		850 mb axis of cold air advection
red (25 KT / 35 KT)	(25 KT / 35 KT)	850 mb shear
brown		700 dry intrusion edge
brown		700 mb moisture
brown		700 mb 12-hr no change (T or hgt)
brown		700 mb temperature ridge
brown		700 mb thermal trough
brown		700 mb convergence zone
brown		700 mb axis of cold air advection
brown (55 KT)	(55 KT)	700 mb jet axis (dry)
brown		700 mb diffluence
brown		700 mb significant height falls
brown		700 mb significant temperature falls

COLOR   **MONOCHROME**

blue		500 mb isotherms
blue		500 mb critical isotherm
blue		500 mb thermal trough
blue	-16	500 mb significant height falls
blue	-4	500 mb significant temperature falls
green		500 mb moisture
yellow		500 mb PVA zone
blue	70 KT	500 mb jet axis
blue		500 mb shear
blue		500 mb diffluence
purple	90 KT	300-200 mb jet axis
purple		300-200 mb jet max
purple		300-200 mb diffluence
purple		300-200 mb shear

Appendix 8. Stability Indices

The long, hard road of understanding the thunderstorm is demonstrated by the plethora of stability indices. Many of them exist as simple rules of thumb, created in a time where calculators and slide rules precluded lengthy calculations for multiple forecast points. Since the 1990s, the explosion of computing power has made computations of integrated stability (CAPE) and shear a relatively trivial process. Therefore the stability parameters in use today are comprised mainly of CAPE, CINH, SRH, and EHI. However the complete set of indices are presented here for the reader's information. It must be remembered that these are all simplifications of very complex processes, and in no way do they replace a meaningful understanding of the sounding. The equations used here are presented in as simple a format as possible. Terms used are T=temperature (deg C), T_d=dewpoint (deg C), D=dewpoint depression (C deg), FF=wind speed (kt); DD=wind direction (deg C). Other terms are explained where they occur.

■ Vertical Totals Index (VT)

The Vertical Totals Index is a measure of the lapse rate from about 5,000 to about 18,000 ft in the atmosphere. It makes no assumptions about parcel temperature. The VT Index was published by Robert Miller in 1967.

VTI = T(850) - T(500).

25 - Storms are unlikely
26 - Scattered thunderstorms
30 - Scattered thunderstorms, a few severe, isolated tornadoes
32 - Scattered to numerous thunderstorms, scattered to a few severe, a few tornadoes
34+ - Numerous thunderstorms, scattered severe storms, scattered tornadoes

■ Cross Totals Index (CT)

The Cross Totals Index relates the low-level moisture to the mid-level temperature, yielding an indirect estimate of lapse rate and convective instability. It was published by Robert Miller in 1967. The Surface Based Cross Totals Index (SCTI) is an alternative index that uses the surface instead of 850 mb.

CTI = T_d(850) - T(500). $CTI = T_d(850) - T(500)$

<17 - Thunderstorms unlikely
18 to 19 - Isolated to few thunderstorms
20 to 21 - Scattered thunderstorms
22 to 23 - Scattered thunderstorms, isolated severe
24 to 25 - Scattered thunderstorms, few severe, isolated tornadoes
26 to 29 - Scattered to numerous thunderstorms, few to scattered severe, few tornadoes
30+ - Numerous thunderstorms, scattered severe, scattered tornadoes

■ Total Totals Index (TT)

The Total Totals Index attempts to integrate the lapse rate information of the Vertical Totals Index with the instability information in the Cross Totals Index. The index is sensitive to steep lapse rates, even if insufficient moisture is present. It was devised by Robert Miller in 1967.

TT = VT + CT

<43 - Thunderstorms unlikely
44-45 - Isolated or few thunderstorms
46-47 - Scattered thunderstorms
48-49 - Scattered thunderstorms, isolated severe
50-51 - Scattered heavy thunderstorms, few severe, isolated tornadoes
52-55 - Scattered to numerous heavy thunderstorms, few to scattered severe, few tornadoes
56+ - Numerous heavy thunderstorms, scattered severe, scattered tornadoes

■ K Index (KI)

This parameter is a sum of lapse rate, 850 mb moisture, and humidity at 700 mb. Humidity at 700 mb is a significant contribution, though this is rare with Great Plains storm events or any event that depends on a mid-level cap. The index was published by J. J. George in 1960.

KI = T(850) - T(500) + T_d(850) - D(700)

<15 - No thunderstorms (0%)
15-20 - Thunderstorms unlikely (<20%)
21-25 - Isolated thunderstorms (20-40%)
26-30 - Widely sct. thunderstorms (40-60%)
30-35 - Numerous thunderstorms (60-80%)
36-40 - Numerous thunderstorms (80-90%)
40+ - Definite thunderstorms (100%)

■ Showalter Stability Index (SSI)

The SSI lifts a parcel from 850 mb to 500 mb. It has the advantage of avoiding the problems inherent with shallow moisture situations, however this comes at the cost of ignoring boundary-layer characteristics. It does not work well in mountainous areas, and cannot be used when the 850 mb level is below ground level. The SSI was developed by Albert Showalter in 1947.

$SSI = T_{ENVIR}(500) - T_{PARCEL}(500)$
for a parcel lifted from 850 mb
>+3: No thunderstorms likely
+3 to +1: Showers probable, thunderstorms
possible
0 to -3: Moderate indication of severe thunderstorms
-4 to -6: Strong indication of severe thunderstorms
<-6: Severe thunderstorms likely

■ Lifted Index (LI)

The Lifted Index was widely favored in 1980s before integrated stability measures became widespread. It lifts a parcel from the surface to 500 mb and compares the parcel temperature to the environmental temperature. The parcel's starting dewpoint should originate from an average mixing ratio of the lowest 100 mb and from the forecast afternoon temperature. The historical origin of the Lifted Index is attributed to Joseph Galway in 1956.

$LI = T_{ENVIR}(500) - T_{PARCEL}(500)$
Parcel lifted from surface
>2 - No significant activity
2 to 0: Showers/thunderstorms possible with other source of lift
0 to -2: Thunderstorms possible
-2 to -4: Thunderstorms probable, only a few severe
<-4: Severe thunderstorms possible

■ Modified Lifted Index (MLI)

The Modified Lifted Index is the same as the Lifted Index except that the parcel is lifted from the highest wet bulb temperature in the lowest 300 mb of the atmosphere. The index was developed by Charles Doswell to better forecast thunderstorms on the High Plains. It was presented as a possible local enhancement to the lifted index, but was adopted for use by the NWS and military forecasters.

$MLI = T_{ENVIR}(500) - T_{PARCEL}(500)$
parcel lifted from maximum wet bulb temperature in lowest 300 mb of atmosphere
Positive: No thunderstorms likely
0 to -2: Showers probable, thunderstorms possible
-3 to -5: Moderate indication of thunderstorms
<-6: Strong indication of severe thunderstorms

Another type of modified lifted index exists which raises a parcel to the -20 deg C isotherm instead of to the 500 mb level. The underlying concept is that a significant thunderstorm should have a cloud temperature of -20 deg C. The historical source of this index is not known.

■ Thompson Index (TI)

The Thompson Index is a combination of Lifted Index and K Index. It attempts to integrate elevated moisture into the index, using the 850 mb dewpoint and 700 mb humidity. Accordingly, it works best in tropical and mountainous locations. The historical origin of the index is not known.

$TI = K - LI$
<u>Over Rockies</u>
<20: Thunderstorms unlikely
20-29: Thunderstorms
30-34: Thunderstorms approaching severe
35+: Severe thunderstorms
<u>East of Rockies</u>
<25: Thunderstorms unlikely
25-34: Slight chance of thunderstorms
35-39: Few widely scattered thunderstorms approaching severe
>40: Severe thunderstorms

■ Severe Weather Threat Index (SWEAT)

The SWEAT index uses a complex set of parameters. It was one of the first indices developed specifically to assess tornado potential. Important parameters are 850 mb dewpoints, lapse rates and parcel instability, wind speed at 850 mb and 500 mb, and directional shear betwen 850 mb and 500 mb. The SWEAT index was published in 1972 by Robert Miller. The index uses the Total Totals Index, which must be computed first.

$SWEAT = 12 \times Td(850) + 20 \times (TT-49) + 2 \times FF(850) + FF(500) + 125 \times (sin[DD(500) - DD(850)] + 0.2)$
<300: Non-severe thunderstorms

300-400: Isolated moderate to heavy thunder-storms

400-500: Severe thunderstorms and tornadoes probable

500-800: Severe thunderstorms and tornadoes likely

800+: Possibly no severe weather (sheared convection)

■ Convective Available Potential Energy (CAPE)

CAPE is currently the most widely used predictor for both thunderstorm potential and severe weather risk. It was defined in 1982 by Morris Weisman and Joseph Klemp. The form of the equation is shown here:

$$CAPE = \left(\sum_{LFC}^{EL} \left[\frac{(T_{ap} - T_e)}{T_e} \vec{g} \right] \right) \Delta z$$

which yields integrated instability in joules per kilogram.

<300: Mostly stable, little or no convection

300-1000: Marginally unstable; weak thunder-storm activity

1000-2500: Moderately unstable; possible severe thunderstorms

2500-3500: Very unstable; severe thunderstorms; possible tornadoes

3500+: Extremely unstable; severe thunderstorms; tornadoes likely

■ Convective Inhibition (CINH)

Convective Inhibition is calculated in the same manner as CAPE except for areas along the parcel lift where the parcel is colder than the surrounding air. In effect, it figures areas that are negatively buoyant. It was developed in 1984 by Frank Colby.

<0: No cap

0 to 20: Weak capping

21-50: Moderate capping

51-99: Strong capping

100+: Intense cap; storms not likely

■ Bulk Richardson Number (BRN)

The Bulk Richardson Number is a ratio between instability and 0-6 km vertical shear. It is a discriminator of storm type, not a predictor. High values indicate unstable and/or weakly sheared environments, while low values indicate weak

instability and/or strong shear. It was defined in 1986 by Morris Weisman and Joseph Klemp.

$BRN = CAPE / [0.5 * U^2]$

where U is the difference in wind speed in meters per secnd between 0 and 6 km

<10: Severe weather unlikely

10-45: Associated with supercell development

>50: Weak multicell storms

■ BRN Shear

BRN shear is simply a measure of the vector difference in the winds through the vertical. The greater the BRN shear, the more likely that a thunderstorm downdraft and precipitation cascade will be separated from the updraft.

$BRN\ Shear = 0.5\ (U_{AVG})^2$

where UAVG is the vector difference between the 0 to 6 km AGL winds and the winds in the lowest 0.5 km of the atmosphere

25-50: Sometimes associated with tornadic storms

50-100: Associated with tornadic storms

■ Energy-Helicity Index (EHI)

EHI is a product of CAPE and 0-6 km shear, thus it is high when either parameter is high. It was developed in 1991 by John Hart and Josh Korotky.

$EHI = (CAPE\ x\ SRH) / 160,000$

1.0-2.0: Heightened threat of tornadoes

2.0-2.4: Tornadoes possible but unlikely strong

2.5-2.9: Tornadoes likely

3.0-3.9: Strong tornadoes possible

4.0+: Violent tornadoes possible

■ Storm Relative Helicity (SRH)

EHI is a product of CAPE and 0-6 km shear, thus it is high when either parameter is high. The SRH is not used widely because it has a high dependence on the correct storm motion vector and it is extremely sensitive to the wind field. The SRH was defined in 1990 by Robert Davies-Jones, Don Burgess, and Mike Foster.

$SRH = \mathbf{w} \cdot (\mathbf{v} - \mathbf{c})\ \Delta z$

where $\mathbf{w} = \mathbf{k}\ x\ d\mathbf{V}/dz$ from 0 to 6 km, $\mathbf{v}$ is the wind vector, and $\mathbf{c}$ is the storm vector

150-299: Weak tornado potential

300-449: Moderate tornado potential

450+: Strong tornado potential

■ KO Index

This index was developed by Swedish meteorologists and used heavily by the Deutsche Wetterdienst. It compares values of equivalent potential temperature at different levels. It was developed by T. Andersson, M. Andersson, and C. Jacobsson, and S. Nilsson.

$KO = 0.5 \times (\theta_e(500) + \theta_e(700)) - 0.5 \times (\theta_e(850) + \theta_e(1000))$

>6: No thunderstorms
2-6: Thunderstorms possible
<2: Severe thunderstorms possible

■ Boyden Index (BI)

This index, used in Europe, does not factor in moisture. It evaluates thickness and mid-level warmth. It was defined in 1963 by C. J. Boyden.

$BI = Z(700) - Z(1000) - T(700) - 200$

    where Z is height in dam

>95: Thunder possible

■ Bradbury Index (BRAD)

Also known as the Potential Wet-Bulb Index, this index is used in Europe. It is a measure of the potential instability between 850 and 500 mb. It was defined in 1977 by T. A. M. Bradbury.

$BRAD = \theta_w(500) - \theta_w(850)$

<3: Thunderstorms possible

■ Rackliff Index (RI)

This index, used primarily in Europe during the 1950s, is a simple comparision of the 900 mb wet bulb temperature with the 500 mb temperature. It is believed to have been developed by Peter Rackliff during the 1940s.

$RI = \theta_w(900) - T_{500}$

>30: Thunderstorms possible

■ Jefferson Index (JI)

A European stability index, the Jefferson Index was intended to be an improvement of the Rackliff Index. The change would make it less dependent on temperature. The version in use since the 1960s is a slight modification of G. J. Jefferson's 1963 definition.

$JI = 1.6 \times \theta_w(850) - T(500) - 0.5 \times (T(700) - T_d(700)) - 8$

>30: Thunderstorms possible

■ S-Index (S)

This European index is a mix of the K Index and Vertical Totals Index. It was designed to be an optimized vertion of the Total Totals Index. The S-Index was developed by the German Military Geophysical Office.

$S = KI - (T(500) + A)$

    where A is 0 if the VT is greater than 25, 2 if the VT is between 22 and 25, and 6 if the VT is less than 22.

<39: No thunderstorms
41-45: Thunderstorms possible
>46: Thunderstorms likely

■ Yonetani Index (YON)

This index was developed by Japanese meteorologist Tsuneharu Yonetani in 1979 to forecast thunderstorms on the Kanto Plain. It provides a measure of conditional instability and low level moisture.

$YON = 0.966\Gamma_L + 2.41(\Gamma_U - \Gamma_W) + 0.966\gamma - 15$

The final term is 16.5 instead of 15 if γ is less than or equal to 0.57. Γ is the layer lapse rate, with U representing 850-500 mb and L representing 900-850 mb, and W is the lapse rate at 850 mb. The term γ is the pressure weighted average of the relative humidity in the 900-850 mb layer, ranging from 0-1.

>0: Thunderstorms likely

■ Potential Instability Index (PII)

This index relates potential instability in the middle atmosphere with thickness. It was defined by A. J. Van Delden in 2001.

$PII = (\theta_e(700) - \theta_e(500)) / (Z(500) - Z(925))$

>0: Thunderstorms likely

■ Deep Convective Index (DCI)

This index is a combination of parcel theta-e at 850 mb and lifted index. This attempts to further improve the lifted index. It was defined by W. R. Barlow in 1993.

$DCI = T(850) + T_d(850) - LI$

10-20: Weak thunderstorms
20-30: Moderate thunderstorms
30+: Strong thunderstorms

Appendix 9. Miller's Severe Weather Parameters

In 1972, Col Robert C. Miller published a list of parameters used by the Air Force Global Weather Central to identify thunderstorm risk areas. It was a basis for techniques used within the National Weather Service and worldwide for decades. Though slightly outdated and not a true ingredients-based approach, it is presented here for its informational value.

Rank	Parameter	Weak	Moderate	Strong
1	500 mb Vorticity	Neutral or Negative Advection	Contours cross vort pattern by <30 deg	Contours cross at more than 30 deg
2	Lifted Index Total Totals	-2 <50	-3 to -5 50 to 55	-6 >55
3	Mid-Level Jet Mid-Level Shear	<35 kt <15 kt per 90 nm	35-50 kt 15-30 kt per 90 nm	>50 kt >30 kt per 90 nm
4	Upper-Level Jet Upper-Level Shear	<55 kt <15 kt per 90 nm	55 to 85 kt 15-30 kt per 90 nm	>85 kt >30 kt per 90 nm
5	Low-level jet	<25 kt	25-34 kt	>34 kt
6	Low-level moisture	<8 g/kg	8-12 g/kg	>12 g/kg
7	850 mb max temp. field	E of moist ridge	over moist ridge	W of moist ridge
8	700 mb height no-change line	Winds cross line <20 deg	Winds cross line 20-40 deg	Winds cross line >40 deg
9	700 mb dry air intrusion	Not available or weak winds	Winds from dry to moist intrude at an angle of 10 to 40 deg are at least 15 kt	Winds intrude at an angle of 40 deg and are at least 25 kt
10	12 hr surface pressure falls	<1 mb	1-5 mb	5 mb
11	500 mb height chg	<30 m	30-60 m	>60 m
12	Height of wet-bulb zero above surface	Above 11,000 ft Below 5,000 ft	9,000-11,000 ft or 5,000-7,000 ft	7,000-9,000 ft
13	Surface pressure over threat area	>1010 mb	1010-1005 mb	<1005 mb
14	Surface dewpoint	<55 deg F	55-64 deg F	>64 deg F

Glossary

This section provides a summary of acronyms that may be encountered in journals, case studies, and forecasting discussions.

ablation Depletion of snow and ice by melting and evaporation.

Ac Altocumulus (q.v.).

AC 1. Convective Outlook bulletin; from the Family of Services data stream header. **2.** Altocumulus

ACARS Aircraft Communications and Reporting System. A block of data transmitted by aircraft that often contains weather data.

ACCAS Altocumulus Castellanus. Altocumulus which forms in a convectively unstable layer.

accessory cloud A cloud which is dependent on a larger cloud system for development.

ACSL Altocumulus standing lenticular (q.v.).

acre-foot The amount of water required to cover one acre to one foot of depth. This equals 326,851 gallons or 43,560 cubic feet.

adiabatic The change in temperature without a transfer of heat. It may be caused by compression or expansion.

advection Horizontal movement of air that causes changes in the physical properties of air at a specific location.

advection fog Fog that forms as warmer, moist air moves over a cold surface. The air is forced to condense as it loses heat to conduction.

advisory In the United States, a weather bulletin which is less serious than a warning.

AFD Area Forecast Discussion (q.v.).

AFGWC Air Force Global Weather Central, which became obsolete on 15 October 1997. It is now known as AFWA.

AFOS Automation of Field Operations and Services (discontinued). The backbone computer system of NWS offices; developed in 1976 and fielded in 1979; retired between 1996 and 1999.

AFWA Air Force Weather Agency (q.v.).

AGL Above Ground Level.

Air Force Weather Agency (AFWA) Weather component of the U.S. Air Force. Activated 15 October 1997, it is a combination of Air Weather Service Headquarters and the Air Force Global Weather Center.

albedo The portion of incoming radiation which is reflected by a surface.

air mass A body of air which contains relatively uniform properties of temperature and moisture.

AJ Arctic jet (q.v.).

algorithm A computer program designed to solve a specific problem. Often used in WSR-88D radars.

aliasing A process in which a radar return has a frequency too high to be analyzed within the given sampling interval but at a frequency less than the Nyquist interval.

ALSTG Altimeter setting (q.v.).

altimeter setting The pressure at which an altimeter must be set so that it reads the correct elevation.

altocumulus Mid-level clouds composed primarily of water or supercooled water. The base is traditionally at a height between 6,500 and 23,000 ft AGL (26,000 ft in the tropics and 13,000 ft at the poles).

Altocumulus Standing Lenticular (ACSL) Clouds formed at the tips of vertical waves in the wake of mountain ranges.

altostratus A bluish veil or layer of clouds having a fibrous appearance. The outline of the sun may show dimly as if through frosted glass. The base is traditionally at a height between 6,500 and 23,000 ft AGL (26,000 ft in the tropics and 13,000 ft at the poles).

anafront Also called *active front*. A cold front in which there is a tendency for air to ascend the frontal surface. Generally associated with lift and weather behind the front. (cf. *katafront*)

anemometer A device that measures wind speed.

ANL Analysis

anomalous propagation Unexpected radio wave propagation that occurs due to non-standard atmospheric conditions. Usually refers to ducting of the beam to the ground, returning ground clutter.

anticyclone An area of high pressure, around which the wind blows clockwise (counterclockwise in the Southern Hemisphere).

anvil The spreading top of a cumulonimbus cloud.

AOA At or above

AOB At or below

AP Anomalous propagation (q.v.)

arctic air Air which has its roots over the snow-covered region of northern Canada, the polar basin, and northern Siberia.

arctic jet Baroclinic jet which develops in association with the polar vortex.

Area Forecast Discussion (AFD) A discussion of the meteorological thinking used in the creation of a zone forecast. (NWS)

ARINC Aeronautical Radio, Incorporated. Company based in Annapolis, MD responsible for ACARS (q.v.)

ARTCC Air Route Traffic Control Center

As Altostratus (q.v.) Also AS.

ASCII American Standard Code for Information Interchange

ASOS Automated Surface Observing System. The network in place across the United States which have provided automated meteorological reports since 1992.

ATTM At this time

AVA Anticyclonic vorticity advection

AVN 1. The NCEP Aviation model, also known as the global spectral model, comprising the United States' primary global weather model; replaced by the GFS model (q.v.) 2. Aviation.

AWC Aviation Weather Center

AWIPS Advanced Weather Interactive Processing System

AWOS Automated Weather Observing System

back door cold front A cold front moving south or southwestward along and near the Appalachians.

backing Referring to a change in wind direction that is counterclockwise, with respect to either height or time. Contrast with *veering*.

backscatter Power that returns to the radar dish after striking a target.

baroclinic zone An area in which a horizontal temperature gradient exists. Rapid weather changes may occur in such zones.

barotropic More properly referred to as *equivalent barotropic*, this term refers to a weather system which has weak or insignificant temperature contrasts

barotropic zone An area in which a significant horizontal temperature gradient does not exist. Rapid weather changes are not as likely as in a baroclinic zone.

Base Reflectivity (BR) A simple reflectivity product as obtained from any elevation of a radar scan (not necessarily the lowest one).

base velocity A simple velocity product as obtained from any elevation of a radar scan (not necessarily the lowest one).

beam width In radar meteorology, the width within which the power density is at least half that of the axis of the beam (i.e. within 3 dB)

blizzard A winter storm which produces, for at least 3 hours, both winds gusting to 35 mph and falling/drifting/blowing snow reducing visibility to less than 1/4 mile.

block A long wave pattern, usually revealed on 200/250/300 mb charts, in which the long waves are neither progressing nor retrogressing. Often refers to the responsible feature, such as an omega or rex block (q.v.)

boundary layer (BL, PBL) The layer in contact with the ground in which friction is significant. This is usually the lowest few thousand feet of the atmosphere but may vary greatly with weather pattern, season, and insolation.

broken Partial coverage of the sky by a layer of more than half (5 to 7 oktas). (cf. *clear, few, scattered,* and *overcast*)

BR Base Reflectivity (q.v.)

BRN Bulk Richardson Number (q.v.)

BUFR Binary Universal Format for Data Representation

Bulk Richardson Number (BRN) The ratio of CAPE to vertical wind shear. It has been found that values of less than 45 support supercellular structures, while greater than 45 favors multicells. However it is not as good of a predictor as its component terms are.

BWER Bounded Weak Echo Region

CAA Cold air advection (q.v.)

cap A layer of warm air aloft that acts as an inversion and suppresses convective development. It may be measured by the Convective Inhibition Index, or CINH (q.v.)

CAPE Convective Available Potential Energy (q.v.)

Cb, CB Cumulonimbus (q.v.)

Cc, CC Cirrocumulus (q.v.)

CCL Convective Condensation Level (q.v.)

Ci, CI Cirrus (q.v.)

CIN Convective inhibition

CISK Convective instability of the second kind

cirrocumulus (Cc) A layer of high, fibrous clouds with convective cells. The cloud is made up entirely of ice crystals. Its bases are traditionally as low as 16,000 ft (20,000 ft in the tropics; 10,000 ft in polar regions).

cirrostratus (Cs) A thin layer of high, fibrous clouds without detail and often appearing as a sheet covering the sky. It is composed entirely of ice crystals. Its bases are traditionally as low as 16,000 ft (20,000 ft in the tropics; 10,000 ft in polar regions).

cirrus (Ci) A layer of high, fibrous clouds composed entirely of ice crystals. Its bases are traditionally as low as 16,000 ft (20,000 ft in the tropics; 10,000 ft in polar regions).

clear Complete absence of cloud. (cf. *few, scattered, broken,* and *overcast*)

cloud height The height of a cloud's base, usually rounded to the nearest hundred feet (thousand feet above 10,000 ft).

cold front The leading edge of an air mass that is replacing a warmer air mass.

Composite Reflectivity (CR) A WSR-88D radar product that displays the maximum reflectivity observed in a grid box at a given location.

confluence A pattern in which wind flows inward into a common axis. It is not the same as convergence. (cf. *difluence, convergence, divergence*)

convection The transport of heat and moisture by the vertical movement of air in an unstable atmosphere. This may cause cumuliform clouds and thunderstorms.

Convective Available Potential Energy (CAPE) the vertically integrated buoyancy of a rising air parcel. Measured in j/kg.

Convective Condensation Level (CCL) The height at which a parcel of air, if heated sufficiently from below, will rise adiabatically until saturation begins.

Convective Inhibition (CIN) A measure of negative buoyancy that prevents a rising parcel from reaching its Level of Free Convection, or LFC (q.v.). It is measured in j/kg.

convective temperature The theoretical surface temperature for a given atmospheric profile that must be reached to start the formation of convective clouds.

convergence A wind pattern in which more air is entering than leaving, either through speed convergence or confluence. (cf. *divergence, difluence, confluence*)

CONUS Continental United States

Coordinated Universal Time (UTC) See Universal Coordinated Time.

COOSAC Committee on Operations, Standards, and Conventions

Coriolis effect The effect caused by the Earth's rotation which deflects parcels to the right (left in the Southern Hemisphere).

COTR Contract Office Technical Representative

couplet Adjacent maxima of radial velocities of opposite signs.

CPC Climate Prediction Center

CR Composite Reflectivity (q.v.)

cross section A diagram of the atmosphere in which horizontal distance is expressed on the X-axis and height on the Y-axis.

Cross Totals index (CT) An expression of instability, equalling $Td_{850}-T_{500}$. Values of greater than 18-30 are considered significant.

Cs, CS Cirrostratus (q.v.)

CSI Conditional symmetric instability

CT Cross Totals index (q.v.)

Cu, CU Cumulus (q.v.)

cumulonimbus (Cb) A large, cauliflower-shaped cloud whose upper portions are usually fibrous. Often associated with precipitation and thunder.

cumulus (Cu) Low, heaplike clouds that are associated with convective weather. The three "categories" of cumulus are typically fair-weather, moderate, and towering. Further cumulus development will evolve into cumulonimbus.

CVA Cyclonic vorticity advection

cyclogenesis The intensification of a low-pressure system.

cyclone An area of low pressure with a closed circulation. The wind flow rotates counterclockwise (clockwise in the Southern Hemisphere).

dBZ Decibels of reflectivity factor.

decoupling The intensification of the contrast between the boundary layer and the free atmosphere, which strengthens winds above and weakens winds below. Tends to occur at night.

DELMARVA Delaware-Maryland-Virginia

derecho A widespread and fast-moving convective windstorm.

difluence Alternate spelling of *diffluence* (q.v.)

diffluence A pattern in which wind flows outward from a common axis. It is not the same as divergence. (cf. *confluence, convergence, divergence*)

diurnal **1.** Occurring on a daily basis. **2.** Occurring during the day. (cf. *nocturnal*)

divergence A wind pattern in which more air is leaving than entering, either through speed divergence or diffluence. (cf. *convergence, diffluence, confluence*)

DOCBLOCK Computer program documentation block

dryline A boundary which separates dry, warm continental air from moist, warm oceanic air. It is most common in the Great Plains, the Sahel, India/Bangladesh, Australia, and China.

dynamics A term that generally refers to forces produced by air out of geostrophic balance which in turn produces vertical motion.

easterly wave A disturbance embedded in the trade winds that moves east to west.

EBDIC Extended Binary-Coded Decimal Interchange Code

ECMWF European Centers for Medium Range Weather Forecasting

EHI Energy Helicity Index (q.v.)

EL Equilibrium Level (q.v.)

EMC Environmental Modelling Center (q.v.)

Energy Helicity Index (EHI) An index that is a product of shear and instability, and is defined as CAPE x SRH / 160,000, where CAPE is j/kg and SRH is in m^2/s^2.

Environmental Modelling Center (EMC) A center of NCEP that is focused on improving numerical modelling technologies.

Equilibrium Level (EL) The height, sometimes within the stratosphere, at which a rising parcel's temperature becomes equal to that of the environment. Upward momentum is sharply lost beyond this point.

ETA Eta model

European Model The ECMWF global spectral model.

Exit region The region downstream from a jet max. The poleward side typically is associated with divergence aloft and upward motion; the equatorward side with convergence aloft and downward motion.

FA Area forecast

FAA Federal Aviation Administration

Family of Services (FOS) The public connection to National Weather Service data which was established in 1983.

FD Winds and temperatures aloft forecast

FEW Partial coverage by cloud material of a quarter or less (1 to 2 oktas). (cf. *clear, scattered, broken, overcast*)

FFG Flash flood guidance

FNL Final production run for a given cycle

FNMOC Fleet Numerical Oceanography Center

FNOC Fleet Numerical Oceanographic Center (obsolete; replaced by FNMOC)

FOS Family Of Services (q.v.)

FT Terminal forecast (obsolete; now TAF)

FTP File Transfer Protocol

FTS Federal Telecommunications System

GBL Global production run for a given cycle

GDAS Global Data Assimilation System production run for a given cycle

GDM Graphic Display Model

geostrophic wind The imaginary wind that would result from a balance of both pressure gradient force and the Coriolis effect.

GES Guess

GFS Global Forecast System (q.v.)

Global Forecast System (GFS) The most sophisticated global spectral model currently used by the United States. It incorporates both the AVN and MRF models, whose names have been "retired".

GMT Greenwich Mean Time

GOES Geostationary Operational Environmental Satellite. The United States' network of geostationary weather satellites poised at the Equator above the Western Hemisphere continuously since 1974.

GRIB Gridded Binary data

GTS Global Telecommunications System

HADS Hydrometeorological Automated Data System

HIC Hydrologist In Charge

HMT Hydrometeorological Technician

hodograph A polar coordinate graph showing the wind profile of the atmosphere at a given point, with respect to ground-relative azimuth and speed.

HPC Hydrometeorological Prediction Center (q.v.)

hurricane A warm-core tropical system that has sustained surface winds exceeding 63 kt.

Hydrometeorological Prediction Center (HPC) A center of NCEP which is responsible for centralized forecasting functions of the National Weather Service.

ICAO International Civil Aviation Organization

IMSL International Mathematical and Statistical Library

instability An atmospheric state in which warm air is able to continue rising and accelerating.

inversion An increase in temperature with height,

comprising a stable layer in the atmosphere. Vertical motion through the inversion is suppressed.

INVOF In vicinity of

IR Infrared

isallobar A line of equal atmospheric pressure change.

isentrope A line of equal potential temperature.

isentropic lift Lift produced by motion of air along surfaces of constant potential temperature which slope upward relative to the parcel's motion. This typically occurs when the parcel is traversing from warmer to colder air below.

isentropic subsidence Sinking motion produced by motion of air along surfaces of constant potential temperature which slope downward relative to the parcel's motion. This typically occurs when the parcel is traversing from colder to warmer air below.

isobar A line of equal pressure.

isochrone A line of equal time.

ISPAN Information Stream Project for AWIPS/ NOAAPORT

J/KG Joules per kilogram

jet max A region of maximum winds within a jet stream. Also *jet streak, speed max.*

jet streak A region of maximum winds within a jet stream. Also *jet max, speed max.*

JIF Job Implementation Form

JMA Japan Meteorological Agency

JSC Johnson Spaceflight Center

JSPRO Joint Systems Program Office for NEXRAD

katafront Also called *inactive front.* A cold front in which there is a tendency for air to descend the frontal surface. Generally associated with subsidence behind the front and weather ahead of the front. (cf. *anafront*)

K-Index (KI) A measure of the thunderstorm potential based on vertical temperature lapse rate, moisture content of the lower atmosphere, and the vertical extent of the moist layer. Equals $T_{850}-T_{500}+Td_{850}-DD_{700}$ where DD equals dewpoint depression. Values above 20-35 are significant.

KI K-Index (q.v.)

knot A measure of velocity, nautical miles per hour, equal to 1.15 statute miles per hour.

lapse rate The change in temperature with height. Normally is 6.5 Celsius degrees per km.

LAWRS Limited Aviation Weather Reporting Station (usually a control tower)

LCN Loosely Coupled Network

LI Lifted Index (q.v.)

LCL Lifted Condensation Level (q.v.)

LEWP Line echo wave pattern

LFC Level of free convection

LFQ Left-front quadrant of a jet streak. In the Northern Hemisphere this is usually associated with upward motion.

LRQ Left-rear quadrant of a jet streak. In the Northern Hemisphere this is usually associated with downward motion.

Lifted Condensation Level (LCL) The height at which a parcel of air will become saturated if lifted adiabatically.

Lifted Index (LI) The temperature difference between a lifted parcel and that of its environment at 500 mb. This is a single-level expression of instability. It equals T_E-T_P where E is the environment and P is the parcel. Negative values are unstable, and below -5 are significant.

LLJ Low Level Jet (q.v.)

Low Level Jet (LLJ) An elongated area of strong winds, generally below 10,000 ft MSL, which may occur in advance of extratropical lows. It is significant in transporting heat and moisture poleward, reinforcing baroclinicity and destabilizing the atmosphere.

long wave A large-scale wave in the upper atmosphere, either a trough or a ridge. There are usually four or five long waves around a hemisphere.

M2/S2 Meters squared per second squared

MAR Modernization and Associated Restructuring Program

MAX Maximum

Maximum Parcel Level (MPL) The highest attainable level a thunderstorm updraft can reach, where all further upward velocity of a parcel is lost. Factors in overshooting tops.

MB Millibars

MCC Mesoscale convective complex

MCD Mesoscale discussion

MCIDAS Man-Computer Interactive Data Access System

MCS Mesoscale Convective System

MDR Manually Digitized Radar (now obsolete)

mesocyclone A low pressure area which is the embodiment of a rotating thunderstorm; it usually measures 1 to 5 miles in diameter. It is a misnomer because it is not a mesoscale system.

mesolow A mesoscale low-pressure area. Not to be confused with mesocyclone.

mesohigh A mesoscale high-pressure area, sometimes associated with stagnating thunderstorm outflow air.

mesoscale Referring to weather systems with scales of about 50 to 500 miles, or 1 to 24 hours.

METAR Meteorological Aviation Report

MIC Meteorologist In Charge

MLCAPE Mean Layer CAPE. Calculated using a parcel that contains mean temperature and mixing ratio of a layer, typically 100 mb deep.

MOA Memorandum of Agreement

Model Output Statistics (MOS) A statistical forecasting model, usually calculated city-by-city.

monsoon A seasonal shift in wind direction.

MOS Model Output Statistics (q.v.)

MOU Memorandum of Understanding

MPL Maximum Parcel Level (q.v.)

MPC Marine Prediction Center

MRF Medium Range Forecast model (obsolete; replaced by GFS)

MSL (above) Mean Sea Level

MSLP Mean Sea Level Pressure

MUCAPE Most Unstable CAPE. CAPE calculated from a parcel that provides the most unstable CAPE possible.

NASA National Aeronautics and Space Administration

National Centers for Environmental Prediction (NCEP) Was NMC (National Meteorological Center) from 1958-1995. An agency falling under NOAA which provides guidance and products to the National Weather Service. It is comprised of nine centers: Aviation Weather Center (AWC); Climate Prediction Center (CPC); Environmental Modelling Center (EMC); Hydrometeorological Prediction Center (HPC); NCEP Central Operations (NCO); Ocean Prediction Center (OPC); Space Environmental Center (SEC); Storm Prediction Center (SPC); and Tropical Prediction Center (TPC).

National Climatic Data Center (NCDC) The United States government agency responsible for archival of meteorological data.

National Oceanic and Atmospheric Administration (NOAA) The United States government agency falling under the Department of Commerce, which is responsible for all civilian programs engaged in work with the atmosphere, oceans, and lakes.

National Weather Service (NWS) A branch of NOAA responsible for all United States public forecasting.

NCCF NOAA Central Computer Facility

NCDC National Climatic Data Center (q.v.)

NCEP National Centers for Environmental Prediction (q.v.)

NCO NCEP Central Operations

negative tilt Description of an upper-level trough whose axis is tilted to the west with increasing latitude. It is often associated with strengthening dynamics.

NESDIS National Environmental Satellite Data and Information Service

NEXRAD Next Generation Weather Radar (WSR-88D)

NEXUS Next Generation Upper-Air System

NGM Nested Grid Model

NHC National Hurricane Center

NIDS NEXRAD Information Dissemination Service

nimbostratus An amorphous cloud thick enough to completely obscure the sun, with its base almost indistinguishable and typically obscured by precipitation. Does not produce showers or thunder. Abbreviated Ns.

NMC National Meteorological Center (obsolete; now NCEP)

NMFS National Marine Fisheries Service

NOAA National Oceanic and Atmospheric Administration (q.v.)

NOS National Ocean Survey

NOTAM Notice to Airmen

nowcast A forecast of about six hours or less. Also called a *short-term forecast*.

Ns Nimbostratus (q.v.)

NS Nimbostratus (q.v.)

NSSFC National Severe Storms Forecast Center

NVA Negative vorticity advection. Advection of negative vorticity into a region.

NWS National Weather Service (q.v.)

NWSTG National Weather Service Telecommunications Gateway

occlusion The convergence of three air masses, in which the least dense is displaced aloft and the remaining two are demarcated by an *occluded front*. Typically occurs when a cold front "catches up" to a warm front.

OFOAR Office of Oceanic and Atmospheric Research

OHP One-Hour Precipitation, as used in weather radar estimates.

OI Optimum Interpolation method

okta An eighth of sky cover.

omega block An upper-level pattern in which a high pressure (height) area intensifies to a very high amplitude, resembling the greek letter omega. It "locks in" the long wave pattern.

ON Office Note

outflow boundary The leading edge of outflow from a thunderstorm downdraft. It may persist hours or days after the dissipation of the storm.

overcast A cloud layer completely covering the sky (8 oktas of cover). (cf. *clear, few, scattered*, and *broken*)

overrunning An oversimplification of the process of *isentropic lift* (q.v.).

PE Primitive Equation model

PFJ Polar front jet (q.v.)

PIREP Pilot Report

polar front jet (PFJ) The jet that is associated with the gradient between polar and tropical air masses. (cf. *arctic jet, subtropical jet, low-level jet*)

polar vortex A large cold-core low aloft that typically is found over northern Hudson Bay in North America during the winter months. Occluding polar front systems are usually absorbed into the polar vortex.

POP Probability of Precipitation (q.v.)

positive area The area formed on a sounding between an environmental temperature line and a warmer parcel temperature line. Its area is roughly proportional to CAPE.

positive-tilt Description of an upper-level trough whose axis is tilted to the east with increasing latitude. It is often associated with weakening dynamics.

potential temperature The temperature which a parcel would have if brought to a common level, by standard convention 1000 mb.

pressure gradient The change in pressure over a given distance.

Probability of Precipitation (POP) A quantity that describes the likelihood of a measurable amount of precipitation at any given location in a forecast area. The NWS expressions are 20% for slight chance, 30-50% for a chance, and 60-70% for likely.

PROD Production (for operational jobs)

profiler Also *wind profiler*. A radio detection device designed to measure wind direction and speed vertically in the troposphere above a given point.

PVA Positive vorticity advection. Equal to CVA in the Northerm Hemisphere and AVA in the Southern Hemisphere (q.v.)

Q vector A horizontal vector representing the rate of change of the horizontal potential temperature gradient. Convergence or divergence of the vectors are associated with forcing for vertical motion.

QG Quasi-geostrophic

QPF Quantitative Precipitation Forecast

RAOB Radiosonde observation

radial velocity The component of motion along an axis extending from a radar unit. The NEXRAD base velocity product depicts radial velocity.

RAFS Regional Analysis and Forecast System (NGM)

range folding A process by which a radar echo returns after another pulse has been transmitted, creating an echo that might be incorrectly distanced by the radar unit.

RAREP Radar Report

RCM Radar Coded Message. An automated product of the WSR-88D unit which provides a summary of the echoes and signatures from a given radar.

rex block A blocking pattern in the upper levels in which a closed high is located poleward of a closed low. The long-wave pattern tends to "lock up".

RFQ Right-front quadrant of a jet streak. In the Northern Hemisphere this is usually associated with downward motion.

RGL Regional Model

ridge An elongated area of high pressure or heights.

RRQ Right-rear quadrant of a jet streak. In the Northern Hemisphere this is usually associated with upward motion.

RUC Rapid Update Cycle model

RUNHIST Run History

SBCAPE Surface based CAPE; resulting from a parcel that is lifted from the surface with no other modifications.

Sc Stratocumulus (q.v.)

SC Stratocumulus (q.v.)

scattered Partial coverage of a cloud layer, covering more than a quarter to half of the sky, of 2 to 4 oktas. (cf. *clear, few, broken*, and *overcast*)

SD **1**. Radar Report (now obsolete) **2**. *Storm*

Data, a publication of NCDC.

SDM Senior Duty Meteorologist

SEC Space Environment Center

Showalter Stability Index (SSI) The difference in temperature between the environment at 500 mb and a parcel lifted from 850 mb, expressed as T_{500}-T_{850}. A negative value corresponds to instability. Lifted Index and CAPE are usually preferred over the SSI.

SIGMET Significant Weather bulletin for pilots

SOO Science and Operations Officer

sounding A plot of temperature and dewpoint above a given station with respect to temperature (X-axis) and height (Y-axis). A thermodynamic diagram, usually the SKEW-T log P, is typically used.

SPC Storm Prediction Center (q.v.)

spectrum width The variance in velocity of scatterers within a given volume of air.

speed max A region of maximum winds within a jet stream. Also *jet max, jet streak.*

SPENES NESDIS satellite precipitation estimate

SRH Storm-relative helicity

SSI Showalter Stability Index (q.v.)

St Stratus (q.v.)

ST Stratus (q.v.)

STJ Subtropical jet (q.v.)

STK Storage Technology

Storm Prediction Center (SPC) A branch of NCEP, located in Norman, Oklahoma, which is responsible for providing short-term forecast guidance for convective storms.

stratocumulus A relatively flat, low cloud with little vertical development. It has distinct globular masses or rolls.

stratus (St) A low, sheetlike cloud which may either occur alone, or with precipitation (in which case it is referred to as *scud, fractus,* or *stratus of bad weather).*

subsidence Sinking motion.

sub-synoptic Mesoscale.

subtropical jet (STJ) An upper-level jet stream that is usually found between 20 and 30 deg of latitude and is associated with thermal differences within the subtropical high. (cf. *arctic jet, polar front jet,* and *low-level jet)*

SWODY1 Severe Weather Outlook - Day 1

SWODY2 Severe Weather Outlook - Day 2

synoptic-scale Spanning a distance scale of over 500 miles or a time scale of days.

TAF Terminal Aerodrome Forecast

TCU Towering Cumulus

TD Tropical Depression

teleconnection A strong statistical relationship between weather in different parts of the globe.

theta-e Equivalent potential temperature

Total Totals Index (TTI) A sum of the Cross Totals and Vertical Totals indices. It is equal to T_{850}-T_{500}+Td_{850}-T_{500}. A value of greater than 44-56 is considered significant.

TPB Technical Procedures Bulletin

TPC Tropical Prediction Center (q.v.)

Tropical Prediction Center (TPC) A branch of NCEP responsible for tropical weather forecasting, including hurricanes.

tropical storm A warm-core storm with a maximum sustained surface wind of 34-63 kt.

tropopause The point between the troposphere and stratosphere at which a positive tropospheric lapse rate becomes neutral or negative.

trough An elongated area of low pressure or heights.

TS Tropical Storm

TTI Total Totals Index (q.v.)

typhoon A tropical storm of hurricane strength in the Western Pacific basin.

UA Pilot Report

UCAR University Corporation for Atmospheric Research

UCL UNICOS Control Language (shell script)

UKMO United Kingdom Met Office

UKMET United Kingdom Met Office

ULJ Upper level jet

UPS Uninterruptable Power Supply

UTC Universal Coordinated Time

UVV Upward vertical velocity

VAD Velocity Azimuth Display. A plot of radial velocity (Y-axis) with respect to azimuth (X-axis) by a weather radar for a given level. It is used as a basis for construction of VWP diagrams (q.v.)

VAFTAD Volcanic Ash Forecast Transport and Dispersion

VC Vicinity

Veering Referring to a clockwise change in the wind direction, with respect to either height or time. Contrast with *backing.*

vertical stack The tendency for a weather system, usually a closed low or high, to have the same location aloft as at the surface. This typically indicates a lack of baroclinicity and suggests a warm-core or cold-core structure.

Vertical Totals index (VT) An expression of the

low to mid-level lapse rate, as given by $T_{850}-T_{500}$. A value of 26 or more is considered significant.

VIL Vertically Integrated Liquid

volume scan The complete scan of a weather radar for all assigned elevations. When a volume scan is complete, the radar is able to generate all possible products (with the exception of products that require a history of an echo). The WSR-88D completes a volume scan in 5 to 10 minutes.

vort max The highest vorticity in a given region.

vorticity The rotation in a volume of air, made up of shear and curvature.

VSB Visible

VWP VAD Wind Profile. A plot of winds with height above a given station, as determined by a weather radar. The profile is displayed with height as the Y-coordinate and time as the X-coordinate.

VT Vertical Totals index (q.v.)

WAA Warm air advection

WAFS World Area Forecast System

WBZ Wet Bulb Zero (q.v.)

Wet Bulb Zero (WBZ) The height at which the wet bulb temperature drops below freezing, expressed as height above ground level (AGL). It is a measure of depth through which a hailstone will melt. Values of less than 10,000 ft are associated with large hail, given enough instability.

WFO Weather Forecast Office

WMSC Weather Message Switching Center

WMO World Meteorological Organization

WS Significant Weather bulletin (SIGMET) for pilots

WSFO Weather Service Forecast Office

WSO Weather Service Office

WST Convective SIGMET for pilots

WW Weather watch (thunderstorm or tornado)

WWB World Weather Building

Z Zulu Time (Greenwich Mean Time)

ZFP Zone Forecast Product (q.v.)

Zone Forecast Product (ZFP) A NWS bulletin that provides a clear, chronological statement of the weather conditions in a county or a given set of counties for the general public.

Suggested Internet Weather Sites

Provided below are some excellent launching points for finding even more weather forecasting charts and diagrams. Have suggestions for the next edition? We'd love to hear about them. E-mail the author at the address listed in the introduction.

❏ Original Sources

When you want an original source of data from a site that actually hosts the graphics, here's where to start.

<www.nco.ncep.noaa.gov/pmb/nwprod/analysis>
NCEP Central Operations / Product Management Branch — Excellent collection of the ETA, GFS, andNGM runs, direct from one of the biggest modelling centers in the world.

<weather.cod.edu>
College of DuPage — The College of DuPage, just west of Chicago, has some of the sharpest minds in operational forecasting as well as a cutting-edge data site to boot.

<www.rap.ucar.edu/weather>
UCAR Real-Time Weather Data — Managed by Greg Thompson at the National Center for Atmospheric Research, this site has been a longtime favorite of many weather hobbyists.

<twister.sbs.ohio-state.edu>
Ohio State University — The OSU weather site is dependable, thorough, and packed with graphics.

❏ Links and Data Listings

Sometimes it can be better to set your browser's start page to a wider variety of data rather than just concentrating on one source. Here are some good options to look through.

<www.stormeyes.org/tornado/rogersif.htm>
Roger Edwards' Storm Intercept Forecasting Links — Not just for storm forecasting. Incredibly thorough.

<www.srh.noaa.gov/faaacademy/ipwb_charts.html>
FAA Academy — Tons of links to charts and satellite photos.

<www.hamwx.com/forecast_links.htm>
HamWX — Steve Miller and Larry Cosgrove's list of numerous weather resources.

<pages.prodigy.net/johnpar>
John Parlagreco's weather page — Nicely organized and fairly exhaustive, created by a Rutgers University research assistant/meteorologist.

<www.stormtrack.org/data>
Stormtrack Data Page — Numerous weather links provided by Kevin Scharfenberg.

<members.lycos.co.uk/david77hayfield/>
David Hayfield's Europe weather site — Lots of links covering Europe.

<www.westwind.ch>
Westwind — A very extensive list of links for European weather

Suggested References and Further Reading

This book is not intended to be authoritative on any of the material presented. Therefore presented here is a list of source materials for this book as well as useful, comprehensive resources that can be sought after for further reading. Internet URL's are provided where applicable.

General forecasting education and reference

Ahrens, C. Donald (1994). *Meteorology Today: An Introduction to Weather, Climate, and the Environment*. West Publishing Co., St. Paul (ISBN 0-314-02779-3). 592 pp.

Carlson, Toby N. (1991). *Mid-Latitude Weather Systems*. Routledge, London (ISBN 0-415-10930-2). 507 pp.

Cole, Franklyn W. (1980). *Introduction to Meteorology*. John Wiley & Sons, New York (ISBN 0-471-04705-8). 505 pp.

Gedzelman, Stanley D. (1980). *The Science and Wonders of the Atmosphere*. John Wiley & Sons, New York (ISBN 0-471-02972-6). 535 pp.

Moran, Joseph M. (1994). *Meteorology: The Atmosphere and the Science of Weather*. Macmillan, Englewood Cliffs (ISBN 0-02-383341-6). 517 pp.

National Weather Service (1993). *Forecasters Handbook No. 1*. 340 pp.

Stull, Roland B. (1995). *Meteorology Today for Scientists and Engineers*. West Publishing Co., St. Paul (ISBN 0-314-06471-0). 385 pp.

Vasquez, Tim (2001). *Weather Forecasting Handbook*. Weather Graphics Technologies, Austin (ISBN 0-9706840-2-9). 204 pp.

Observational charts

Doswell, Charles A. III (1986). The human element in weather forecasting. *Nat. Wea.*
Dig., **11**, 6-18. <www.cimms.ou.edu/~doswell/human/Human.html>

Djuric, Dusan (1994). *Weather Analysis*. Prentice-Hall, Englewood Cliffs (ISBN 0-13-501149-3). 304 pp.

Miller, Robert C. (1972). *Notes on Analysis and Severe-Storm Forecasting Procedures of the Air Force Global Weather Central*. AWS Technical Report 2000 (Rev), Air Weather Service, Scott AFB. 190 pp.

National Weather Service (1993). *Graphical Guidance*. National Weather Service, Washington. 169 pp.

Sanders, Frederick and Doswell, Charles A. III (1992). A Case for Detailed Surface Analysis. *Bull. of the Amer. Met. Soc.*, **76**, 505-521.

Young, G. S. and Fritsch, J. M. (1989). A Proposal for General Conventions in Analyses of Mesoscale Boundaries. *Bull. of the Amer. Met. Soc.*, **70**: 1412-1513. <ams.allenpress.com>

Satellite Imagery

Cooperative Program for Operational Meteorology, Education, and Training (COMET). COMET Satellite Meteorology Course: Meteorological Sounders. University of Wisconsin homepage. <cimss.ssec.wisc.edu/goes/comet/sounder.html>

National Environmental Satellite, Data, and Information Service (1983). *The GOES Users Guide*, NESDIS, Washington. 164 pp.

NOAA Satellite and Information Services. NOAASIS homepage. <noaasis.noaa.gov/NOAASIS>

Schmit, Timothy J., Wade, Gary S., and Aune, Robert M. (1998). Automated GOES Sounder Products. *Proceedings of the Satellite Applications Conference*, March 4-6, 1993, Asheville. <cimss.ssec.wisc.edu/goes/sounder/products.html>

Radar

Allen, S. (1996). Impacts of Optimum Slant Range on WSR-88D VAD Wind Profiles. NWS Houston homepage. <www.srh.noaa.gov/ftproot/HGX/HTML/projects/vad2/main.htm>

Office of the Federal Coordinator for Meteorology (2003). Part A: System Concepts, Responsibilities, and Procedures. *Federal Meteorological Handbook #11: WSR-88D Doppler Radar Meteorological Observations* (FCM-H11A-2003), OFCM, Washington. <www.ofcm.gov/fmh11/fmh11.htm>

Collins, W. G. (2000). The Quality Control of Velocity Azimuth Display (VAD) Winds at the National Centers for Environmental Prediction. *Preprints, 11th Symposium on Meteorological Observations and Instrumentation*, Albuquerque, NM, Amer. Met. Soc., 317-320. <www.emc.ncep.noaa.gov/mmb/papers/collins/preprints/vadqc.htm>

U. S. Air Force (1992). *WSR-88D Products*. Study Guide C40ST2524 009-SW-101C, Chanute Training Center, Chanute AFB. 42 pp.

Webber, Richard D. (1996). Forecasting Turbulence and Icing using the WSR-88D VAD Wind Profile Product. NWS CR Applied Research Paper ARP20-11. <www.crh.noaa.gov/techpapers/arp20/20-11.html>

Miscellaneous

Beran, D.W. and Wilfong, T.L. (1998). *U.S. Wind Profilers: A Review* (FCM-R14-1998). Office for the Federal Coordinator of Meteorology, 56 pp. <www.ofcm.gov/r14/front.htm>

United Kingdom Met Office (2003). CWINDE Network. Met Office homepage. <www.metoffice.gov.uk/research/interproj/cwinde>

Numerical Models

Allen, C., Kramer, D., Smith, R., and Stults, A. (2001). Vertical Resolution and Coordinates. Texas A&M University homepage. <www.met.tamu.edu/class/metr452/models/2001/vertres.html>

Canadian Meteorological Center (2003). GEM: The Global Environmental Multiscale Model. CMC homepage. <www.cmc.ec.gc.ca/rpn/gef_html_public>

Carr, Frederick H. (1988). *Introduction to Numerical Weather Prediction Models at the National Meteorological Center*. 63 pp.

Evenson, Eric C. and Strobin, Mark H. (1998). Model Boundary Layer Problems and Their Impact on Thunderstorm Forecasting in the Western United States. NWS WR Technical Attachment TA 98-20. <www.wrh.noaa.gov/wrhq/98TAs/9820>

Fleet Numerical Meteorology and Oceanography Center (2002). Model Characteristics and Tendencies for NOGAPS 4.0, COAMPS 3.0, and WW3 1.18. FNMOC homepage. <https://www.fnmoc.navy.mil/PUBLIC/MODEL_REPORTS/MODEL_TENDENCY_REVIEW/tendencies.html>

Hydrometeorological Prediction Center (2003). Model Biases. NCEP homepage. <www.hpc.ncep.noaa.gov/mdlbias/biastext.shtml>

Japan Meteorological Agency (2002). Outline of the Operational Numerical Weather Prediction at the Japan Meteorological Agency. *Appendix to WMO Numerical Weather Prediction Progress Report.* <www.jma.go.jp/JMA_HP/jma/jma-eng/jma-center/nwp/outline-nwp/index.htm>

National Meteorological Center (1987). Section 2.2.1: The NMC Production Suite. *NMC Handbook.*, National Meteorological Center, Washington.

National Weather Service, Binghamton Office (2003). Information on Operational Models. NWS Binghamton homepage. <www.erh.noaa.gov/er/bgm/models.htm>

Staudenmaier, Mike, Jr. (1997). The Navy Operational Global Atmospheric Prediction System (NOGAPS). NWS WR Technical Attachment TA97-09. <www.wrh.noaa.gov/wrhq/97TAs/TA9709/ta97-09.html>

Toth, Zoltan and Kalnay, Eugenia (1997). Ensemble Forecasting at NCEP and the Breeding Method. *Mon. Wea. Rev.*: **125**, 3297-3319. <www.atmos.umd.edu/~ekalnay/TothKalnay97.pdf>

United Kingdom Met Office (2003). *NWP Gazette*, quarterly. <www.metoffice.gov.uk/research/nwp/publications/nwp_gazette>

University Corporation for Atmospheric Research (2003). Operational Models Matrix: Characteristics of Operational NWP Products. UCAR Homepage. <meted.ucar.edu/nwp/pcu2>

Weickman, Klaus, Whitaker, Jeff, Roubicek, Andres, and Smith, Catherine. The use of ensemble forecasts to produce improved medium range (3-15 days) weather forecasts. NCEP Homepage. <www.cdc.noaa.gov/spotlight/12012001>

Text

Office of the Federal Coordinator for Meteorology (1998). *Federal Meteorological Handbook #1: Surface Weather Observations and Reports* (FCM-H1-1998). OFCM, Washington. <www.ofcm.gov/fmh-1/fmh1.htm>

Office of the Federal Coordinator for Meteorology (1997). *Federal Meteorological Handbook #3: Rawinsonde and Pibal Observations* (FCM-H3-1997). OFCM, Washington. <www.ofcm.gov/fmh3/text/default.htm>

Office of the Federal Coordinator for Meteorology (1998). *Federal Meteorological Handbook #12: United States Meteorological Codes and Coding Practices* (FCM-H12-1998). OFCM, Washington. <www.ofcm.gov/fmh12/frontpage.htm>

World Meteorological Organization (1988). *Manual on Codes.* WMO Publication No. 306, World Meteorological Organization, Geneva

Index

Symbols

1000-500 mb thickness 20
1000-700 mb thickness 20
1000-850 mb thickness 20
200 mb 18
250 mb 18
300 mb 18
500 mb 16
540 dam line 20
700 mb 14
850 mb 12

A

absolute vorticity 24
adiabats 30
advection 20, 24
analysis 8
anticyclonic flow 18
anticyclonic rotation 62
anticyclonic vorticity advection 24
ascent 2, 22, 28
AVA 24
Aviation Model 108
AVN 108

B

baroclinic zones 9
baroclinicity 16
base reflectivity 58
beam width 70
Boyden Index 149
Bradbury Index 149
bright band 58
BRN 148
BRN Shear 148
Bulk Richardson Number 148

C

cap 14
CAPE 30, 148
chaff 59, 66
CINH 148
clear air mode 55, 56, 58
cloud code groups 141
cold advection 24
composite reflectivity 60
Convective Availability of Potential Energy 30
Convective Available Potential Energy 148
Convective Inhibition 148
Convective Outlook 86
convergence 2, 62
Coordinated Universal Time 4
couplet 62
Cross Totals Index 146
CT 146
CVA 3, 24
cyclonic flow 18
cyclonic rotation 62
cyclonic vorticity advection 3, 24

D

dam 20
Deep Convective Index 149
dekameters 20
descent 22, 28
descriptors 139
diagnosis 8
divergence 3, 62
dry adiabats 30
drylines 9
dynamics 2

E

Echo Tops 70
ECMWF 116
EFR 120
EHI 148

elevated mixed layer 14
Elevated TVS 78
elevation gaps 70
EML 14
Energy-Helicity Index 148
enhanced imagery 44
ensemble 98, 100
Eta 102
ETVS 78
European Centre for Medium-Range Weather Forecasts 116

F

Fengyun 37
field of view 50
Fleet Numerical Meteorology Center 112
FNMOC 112
forcing 2
four-cell concept 2
Free Text Message 82
frontal systems 12
frontogenesis 28
frontolysis 28
fronts 9, 10
   placement 9
FTM 82
further reading 161
FY 37

G

gate-to-gate shear 62
GDAS 108
GEM 120
geostationary satellites 36
geostrophic balance 2
GFS 108
global 94
Global Data Assimiliation System 108
Global Environmental Multiscale 120
Global Forecast System 108
Global Spectral Model 108